Making the Most of Your LATHE

Patrick Stephens Limited, a member of the Haynes Publishing Group, has published authoritative, quality books for enthusiasts for more than twenty years. During that time the company has established a reputation as one of the world's leading publishers of books on aviation, maritime, military, model-making, motor cycling, motoring, motor racing, railway and railway modelling subjects. Readers or authors with suggestions for books they would like to see published are invited to write to: The Editorial Director, Patrick Stephens Limited, Sparkford, Nr Yeovil, Somerset, BA22 7JJ.

Making the Most of Your LATHE

Harold & Audrey Mason

Patrick Stephens Limited

To
Bill Stanton and Lindsay Todd
who made us believe it was possible

First published in 1992

British Library Cataloguing in
Publication Data
A catalogue record for
this book is available
from the British Library

   ISBN 1-85260-304-6

Library of Congress catalogue card
number 91-71110

Patrick Stephens Limited is part of the
Haynes Publishing Group P.L.C.,
Sparkford, Nr Yeovil, Somerset,
BA22 7JJ.

Printed in Great Britain by J. H. Haynes
& Co. Ltd.

CONTENTS

Introduction

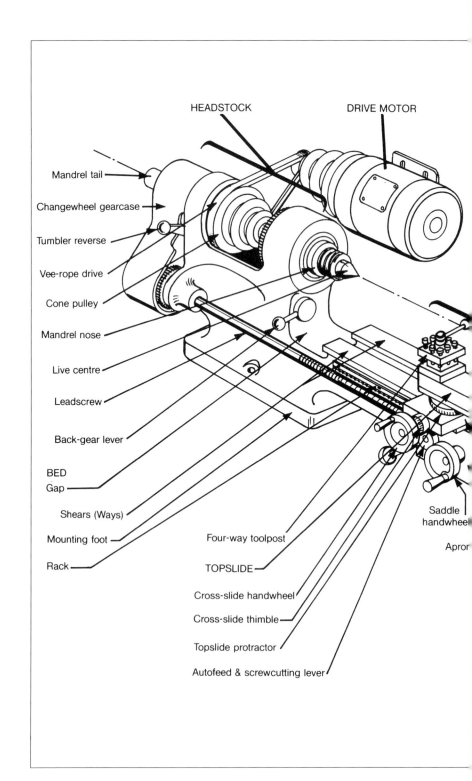

HEADSTOCK

DRIVE MOTOR

Mandrel tail

Changewheel gearcase

Tumbler reverse

Vee-rope drive

Cone pulley

Mandrel nose

Live centre

Leadscrew

Back-gear lever

BED
Gap

Shears (Ways)

Mounting foot

Rack

Four-way toolpost

TOPSLIDE

Cross-slide handwheel

Cross-slide thimble

Topslide protractor

Autofeed & screwcutting lever

Saddle
handwheel

Apron

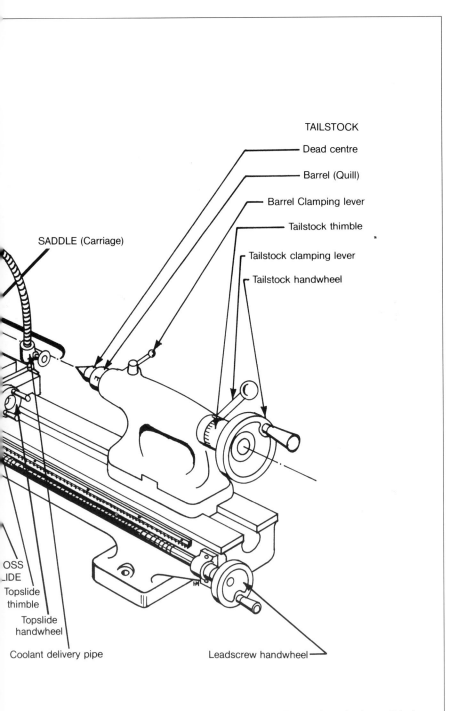

TAILSTOCK

Dead centre

Barrel (Quill)

Barrel Clamping lever

Tailstock thimble

Tailstock clamping lever

Tailstock handwheel

SADDLE (Carriage)

OSS
_IDE
Topslide
thimble

Topslide
handwheel

Coolant delivery pipe

Leadscrew handwheel

Fig. 1. A typical small lathe.

INTRODUCTION

Before you turn the page, wait. This isn't going to be one of those introductions that put you to sleep before you can get your teeth into the text. We hope to whet your appetite and leave you eager to come to grips with the projects we have in store for you.

If you've never used a lathe before we'll lead you through the things you need to know in order to get the best out of being a lathe owner, and along the way you'll build up an arsenal of useful bits of workshop equipment. Audrey has played a major part in the completion of all the items shown in the photographs, but last year, when we suggested this book to the publishers, she had never laid hands on a metal turning lathe. By following the text, studying the drawings and simply diving in at the deep end, she became quite a competent centre lathe turner in a matter of weeks.

In writing this book we chose the approach of 'learning by doing'. Right from the beginning you will get your hands dirty doing most of the jobs a lathe is capable of, and you won't be making 'test pieces' to be displayed on the mantel shelf for a week or two and then flung in the scrap bin. You'll be making things you will probably still be using in 20 years time.

'In at the deep end' may have caused some of you a tremor of self doubt. Let us reassure you. At the outset, no assumptions are made about what you know — or don't know — about lathework. Detailed instructions and examples are given until you are well launched on your adventure. At that point we do start making some assumptions — for example, we assume that by Chapter 8 you won't need to be told how to grip a piece of bar in a four-jaw chuck — which increase as the chapters progress.

The process of decreasing the amount of 'spoon feeding' as the book progresses doesn't just apply to the practical aspects of metalwork. We hope you'll also develop your potential as a designer and your capacity to look critically at the things other people make. With this object in view, we have added a glossary of the terms used in the text and a list of suggested reading to widen your knowledge of the field. We will be overjoyed if droves of you develop a taste for finding out everything you can about this amateur engineering lark. Soak up all you can of the wide variety of printed matter there is available on your pet subject, whether it be steam engines, workshop equipment, clocks or whatever. And don't take any of it at its face value. But above all, test out the claims, build the projects and find out for yourself!

You'll find no advice in this book about which lathe to buy or how much tooling and equipment you need. There are already plenty of places you can go to find that out. Our task has been to get you hooked and send you hurrying for the materials shops to load yourselves up with the stuff you need to build all the projects in the ensuing pages.

However, we must stress, from the word go, the importance of safe working, the ability to get to the end of a job with no broken tools or broken bones. This is our safety code and we feature it here, in the introduction, to stress its importance.

CLOTHING: Don't wear loose sleeves, baggy pullovers or anything likely to be dragged into machinery. Keep sleeves short or roll them back. Wear a leather apron for welding or silver soldering.

HEAD: Keep the headroom in your workshop clear of hanging objects. If you can't avoid them wear a hard hat. Fasten back long hair or wear a cap.

EYES: Wear eye protection on all machines, especially grinders, and during silver soldering and welding.

FINGERS: Have a well stocked first aid box handy with dressings for cuts, scalds and burns. If a job carries a risk of scraping or trapping the fingers wear safety gloves. Never leave the chuck key in the chuck after use.

LUNGS: In all dusty or toxic-fuming operations wear a respirator or at least a suitable face mask with filter pads. Have the workshop well ventilated when using adhesives, solvents, spray paint or gases.

STOMACH: Treat chemical products with extreme caution. Read and comply with the maker's instructions and store chemicals safely out of reach of children.

FEET: Protect your feet against damage by sharp or falling objects with a pair of safety shoes or boots.

BACK: Watch out when lifting heavy equipment or lifting in a confined space. If in doubt, get assistance — either human or mechanical.

ELECTRICITY: *Household mains voltage can kill you!* Always treat electrical equipment with the greatest of respect and ensure that all power is turned off before working on it. If in doubt *leave it alone* and get qualified help. Be sure to switch off power to the lathe motor before making belt or gear changes.

INVEST: Buy a suitable fire extinguisher and store it where it is readily available.

Use safe working practices and your days in the workshop will be happy and numerous, and will go on as long as you do.

It only remains for us to point out some important things about the text which may throw you, on first sight. None of the drawings carries a material specification because we expect you to use bright mild steel or free-cutting BMS (*see Glossary*) unless another material, such as silver steel or brass, is suggested. At this point you may not want to take on the problems that less tractable kinds of steel would give you.

Then we come to the question of the units we choose to use in measuring our work. The amateur engineering world has not yet opened up its heart to the metric system, and we decided this book would be of wider appeal if we used imperial units but also added the metric equivalent for comparison and as a guide for those readers who would find it helpful. On all drawings and in the text, therefore, every inch measurement is followed by its near equivalent in millimetres. It's not so easy when we come to thread sizes and types, so we've simply added a near equivalent metric thread option after each imperial thread specification. It's entirely up to you which you use, so long as you remember to change your tapping drill sizes.

That's all we have to say, except to wish you luck in your endeavours. We hope you enjoy ploughing your way through this book as much as we have enjoyed putting it together.

We could not have contemplated writing this book without the generous help and encouragement of our many friends in the hobby, in the model engineers' supplies trade and in the full-sized world of engineering. You are too many for us to name you individually without the risk of someone being overlooked. May we simply offer our thanks to you all and our wishes for your future good health, success and prosperity.

Harold and Audrey Mason
Outwood, January 1992

1 TOOLMAKER'S BUTTONS

You will have seen the drawing of a typical modeller's lathe at the beginning of the book (**Fig. 1**). Have a good look at it before you do anything else. Don't try to memorise the names of all its parts, that will happen naturally as we get on with our work. This preliminary inspection is simply to ensure that we are speaking roughly the same language in our discussion of what you can do with your lathe now that you've got it.

This is not an armchair book – this is a 'hands-on' guide to getting the best out of your newly acquired lathe. Take the book out into your workshop and prop it up somewhere, not too close to the lathe but where you can quickly refer to it. First look at **Figs. 2** and **3**. This is a toolmaker's button and you're going to

Fig. 2. Setting toolmaker's buttons, using slip-blocks.

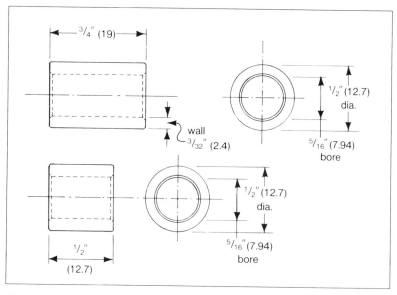

Fig. 3. Details of toolmaker's buttons.

make two of them. We'll go into what you need them for, later.

Grip a piece of ⅝ in (16 mm) diameter Bright Mild Steel (BMS) bar in the three-jaw chuck with 1 in (25.4 mm) sticking out in front of the jaws. Tighten it well – we'll be doing all the operations at the one setting. Clamp a turning-and-facing tool

Fig. 4. Setting a lathe tool on centre height with a height gauge. Note also the saddle clamping screw (bottom left hand corner).

(see **Fig. 124**, to be found at the end of the book) in the toolpost at centre height, and if you are using a four-way toolpost make sure it is clamped down too (**Fig. 4**).

Now turn the chuck by hand a couple of times. You will find that bar sometimes slips between two of the jaws rather than being held by all three, and it will wobble as you turn the chuck. You can imagine what might happen if you ran the lathe under power with the bar not properly gripped. Let's assume you did it right and the bar runs true.

Set the spindle speed at about 650 rpm (less, rather than more) and the carriage feed at 2½ or 3 thou per rev (a thou is 0.001 in (0.025 mm) or one thousandth of an inch). Check that all is clear of the chuck jaws and start the lathe. Turn the cross slide feed handle until the tool barely marks the work, making a bright line on the dark grey surface of the bar. Hold the handle tightly at that position and turn the dial to zero. (If you don't have zeroing dials, stick a little square of marking tape next to the appropriate division on the dial and work from that.) You'll notice that the slides don't move at once, when you turn the handle. The feedscrew handles will revolve quite a way before any movement of the topslide or cross slide happens. This is called backlash. You allow for backlash by ensuring that you keep the slide moving in one direction as you make cuts. If you have to reverse movement for any reason bring the slide back well beyond the required point and wind it forward again to where you want it. This will eliminate the effect of backlash and it's a habit you'll quickly learn. Rack the carriage to the right until the tool point is clear of the work before putting on the cut, which you do by turning the cross slide feed handle clockwise until the dial reads about 5 thou (0.13 mm).

Engage the auto feed by pushing down the handle until you feel it grip the leadscrew, and at the same time turn on the coolant (if you use it). Do not let anything distract you at this point or, before you know what's happening, the tool will hit the chuck jaws with consequences we won't dwell on. If anything does distract you – before you take your eyes off the machine, disengage the auto feed and stop the lathe. This is not being paranoid about unlikely accidents. This is developing good, safe working practices so that you'll end your engineering days with all your fingers intact.

When the tool gets within ¼ in (6.4 mm) of the chuck jaws, disengage the feed and rack the carriage away to the right. Now have a good look at the surface you've cut on your workpiece. If the tool is nice and sharp, you should have a reasonably smooth surface with no obvious 'gramophone' grooves in it.

The next job is to measure the diameter of the newly cut cylinder to find out how much more metal we have to take off to get it down to finished size – in this case, ½ in or 0.500 in (12.7 mm). To do the measuring we prefer a micrometer, although a vernier or dial caliper will do almost as well. We've made our cylinder out of ⅝ in BMS round bar, and we should expect this to be up to 2 thou down on its 'nominal' diameter (the size it is sold as) before we cut into it. Before we get on with the turning we must do a little working out.

- The size we started with could have been 0.623 in (15.82 mm) (⅝ in is 0.625 in or 15.88 mm)
- We took off 5 thou *from each side*, so we reduced the *diameter* by 10 thou.

Take a measurement with your micrometer (see **Fig. 10**). What does it read? If it is around the 0.613 in (15.6 mm) mark we're doing alright, but we have to reduce the diameter to 0.5 in (12.7 mm). It's not advisable to take it all off at once; better to take it in stages.

- Diameter now   0.613 in (15.6 mm)
- Required diameter   0.500 in (12.7 mm)
- To be removed   0.113 in (2.9 mm)

The diameter has to lose 113 thou (2.9 mm) somehow, but remember our earlier warning. When we take a cut of 10 thou (0.25 mm) we reduce the diameter by 20 thou (0.5 mm). So if we want to reduce it by 113 thou (2.9 mm) we need cuts that total 56½ thou (1.45 mm). Let's say five successive cuts of 10 thou (0.25 mm) and we'll check again when we've done that. Follow the procedure we've just carried out, using the same speed and auto feed. When you've taken off your five cuts at 10 thou (0.25 mm), stop the lathe without disturbing the cross slide setting, wind the carriage out of the way and measure the diameter again. You should have about 6 thou (0.15 mm) to remove to reach the finished size.

In order to achieve a superb finish on the outside surface of

Fig. 5. Setting a T&F tool to turn and face. Stoning the top face before finishing cuts.

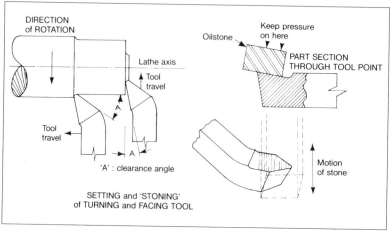

DIRECTION of ROTATION

Lathe axis

Tool travel

Tool travel

'A' : clearance angle

SETTING and 'STONING' of TURNING and FACING TOOL

Oilstone

Keep pressure on here

PART SECTION THROUGH TOOL POINT

Motion of stone

our toolmaker's buttons, we'll drop the feed speed to 1½ or 2 thou (0.04 mm to 0.05 mm) per rev. And – just to make sure – we'll very carefully oilstone the *top face* of the cutting tool as shown in **Fig. 5** (if you stone the *front* face you'll alter the amount taken off at the next cut). Work out exactly how much cut you need to put on, as we did earlier, and set it on the cross-slide feed dial. Apply coolant or neat cutting oil and make your final pass – but this time stop the lathe before you rack the carriage out of the way. You're in for a thrill when you check the diameter and it reads dead on 0.500 in (12.7 mm). If it's more than that, no problem. Take another very fine cut and you'll be there. If it's less than 0.500 in (12.7 mm) there are still one or two things you can do.

If you are adamant that ½ in (12.7 mm) dia buttons are what you want, put the bar aside and get a fresh piece. There will be lots of jobs you can use it for in the future. If you wish, you could simply turn the bar end-for-end and start again at the uncut end. If you're not going to insist on ½ in diameters, settle for a smaller diameter – perhaps ⁷⁄₁₆ in (0.4375 in or 11.1 mm) – and turn your way down to that, in exactly the same way as before. However, this has some snags attached, which will emerge when we come to use the buttons in Chapter 9. For the moment, we're going to assume everyone has the diameter they wanted and we can proceed to the next stage. We've cleaned up the diameter, now we have to clean up the end. This is called 'Facing' the bar and is done with the same tool we used on the diameter. When facing, the tool travels at right angles to the bed shears and the cut is put on with the *topslide* feed handle. You'll find this works better if you clamp the saddle to the bed before you begin facing. There's usually an allen screw or a hexagon-

Fig. 6. Centre-drilling toolmaker's button blanks with a centre drill in a morse taper shank holder. Note the lathe tools covered with plastic pipe.

headed setscrew at the back of the saddle for the purpose (**Fig. 4**).

Take one or two fine cuts across the end and make sure there's no 'pip' left in the middle to divert the point of the drill which is coming next. When the face is to your satisfaction, wind back the cross slide to get the tools out of your way, remembering to wrap the exposed ones with rags or cover with plastic pipe, if yours is a four-way toolpost (it's easier on the hands!). Put a centre drill – in its holder or in a drill chuck – into the tailstock and bring it up into position for drilling the end of the bar without too much tailstock barrel showing (**Fig. 6**). The closer the drill point is to the tailstock casting the less deflection there will be when the cutting edges strike metal. Gently feed in the centre drill until you have a cone-shaped depression of about 3/16 in (4.8 mm) dia in the end of the bar. We like to brush on neat cutting oil for this job, coolant tends to obscure the view. But for the next part – drilling out to a diameter of 5/16 in (8 mm) in stages – coolant is ideal.

If you haven't already put a drill chuck in the tailstock do it now, for deep drilling (**Fig. 7**). Begin with a 1/8 in (3.2 mm) diameter drill and take it in to about 3/4 in (19 mm) depth with frequent withdrawals to clear the flutes of swarf. Some lathes have a graduated thimble on the tailstock handwheel, otherwise

Fig. 7. Finish-drilling a toolmaker's button with a 5/16 in (8 mm) drill in tailstock drill-chuck. The graduations on the tailstock barrel can be seen (right centre).

Fig. 8. Set up for parting-off. The coolant flow is directed into the groove. A single flute countersink bit is gripped in the tailstock chuck.

read off the measurement on the tailstock barrel. Change to a ¼ in (6.4 mm) dia drill and proceed as before until you feel the resistance when the drill point reaches the bottom of the ⅛ in (3.2 mm) hole. Finish out the hole with a sharp ⁵⁄₁₆ in (8 mm) dia drill. There is really no need to ream the hole unless you hate drill bores so much you simply must clean them out.

Before moving the tailstock, change the drill for a ⅝ in (16 mm) dia countersink and lightly chamfer the inside edge of the hole (**Fig. 8**). Take off the sharp outside edge with a fine file. Change the turning and facing tool for a ⅛ in (3.2 mm) wide parting off tool (see **Fig. 124**) and move the tailstock to the end of the bed. To be on the safe side, remove the countersink and the chuck before you go any further. Now, you must change the spindle speed, reducing the rpm (revolutions per minute) to about 200. On our lathe, that's the lowest 'open drive' speed (the lowest without using back gear). Opinions differ on what is the best speed for parting off but we've found low speed and medium-but-firm feed work well for us. We also use plenty of coolant directed right into the groove (**Fig. 8**).

Having the tool point set a little below centre-height cuts down the chances of the tool digging-in. Check that the toolpost is not overhanging the topslide ways, the parting tool is set square to the work and at the correct distance from the end of the work, say ¾ in (19 mm) with an allowance for cleaning up. Lock the saddle, then you're ready to start the lathe and feed in the tool with the cross-slide handle. Direct coolant into the groove and go on feeding in until the button breaks free and drops into the swarf tray. *STOP the lathe* before you try to retrieve it!

Wrap a strip of 1-thou shim (*see Glossary*) around the outside diameter, take the stub of bar out of the chuck and put in the

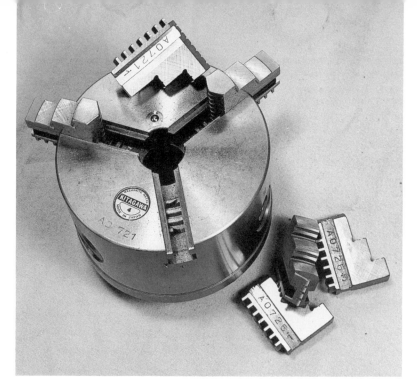

Fig. 9. A three-jaw self-centring chuck with one 'bar' jaw removed to reveal the spiral. Lower right: the extra set of 'disc' jaws.

button with 'parted' end outwards. Tighten the jaws just enough to hold the button, otherwise – even with shim around it – you'll mark the surface. Return the turning-and-facing tool to the toolpost, clamp saddle, increase spindle speed to 650 rpm and clean up the face of the button. Take off the sharp edge with a fine file, countersink lightly and it's finished.

You need at least two toolmaker's buttons and one should be longer than the other. We suggest you make one ½ in (12.7 mm) tall and the other ¾ in (19 mm) tall. If you wish, you can make a pair of holding-down washers too, but it is advisable to wait until you've gone a little further into the book before you break off to do that.

Now it's time for us to explain a few things which we glossed over earlier, so let's begin by looking more closely at the chuck we've just been using (**Fig. 9**). The three-jaw self-centering (SC) chuck is the most used of the three types of lathe workholder at your disposal. The others are the four-jaw independent chuck and the faceplate, but we'll be looking at those later.

The three-jaw SC chuck consists of a body, housing three gripping jaws at 120° to each other, and a backplate by which the chuck is fixed to the lathe mandrel. A new SC chuck should come equipped with two sets of jaws, we will refer to these as the *DISC* jaws and the *BAR* jaws. The jaws move along grooves machined in the body and they are driven by a spiral plate which meshes with teeth cut into the backs of the jaws. The spiral plate is rotated by putting the chuck key into one of the three square sockets and turning it – clockwise to tighten and anticlockwise to slacken the jaws.

The self-centring chuck gets its name from the fact that when you tighten the jaws on a circular workpiece its centre is automatically brought into line with the lathe mandrel axis. Or, it would in an ideal world! In this far-from-ideal world, you can't expect your three-jaw chuck to give you better than a run-out of between 2 (0.05 mm) and 5 (0.13 mm) thou. For all practical purposes this level of error is acceptable. If you want more accuracy you can get three-jaw SC chucks with adjustment screws on the body or the backplate which allow you to eliminate run-out altogether. Most of the time – as when we turned the whole of our toolmaker's button at one chuck setting – you can ignore the error. But you'd be wise to bear it in mind, for the times when it might become a problem.

The material we want you to use for all the projects in this book, unless we specify otherwise, is BMS round bar. In some quarters it is known as Bright Drawn Mild Steel, but BMS will do for our purposes and it's a term that is recognised by your suppliers. You'll quickly pick up the jargon, and learn the common stock sizes that are available, by collecting catalogues and studying advertisements in the model engineering magazines. You'll hear and read about Free Cutting BMS, which is mild steel with a little lead added to its composition to make it easier to cut. It is used in the mass-production of small parts such as nuts and bolts. Get some and try it out – you'll be interested in the differences from machining plain mild steel.

We'd rather not get too involved in a study of lathe tools at this stage. The chart at the back of the book (**Fig. 124**) gives lots of useful information about shapes and grinding angles, but we want you to find out most of what you need to know by using the tools to make things. We can back-track occasionally, as we are doing now, to clarify a point without bringing the whole show to a dead stop. The tools are usually clamped into the toolpost with packings or screw adjustment to bring their cutting edges up to centre height. In the case of a four-way toolpost the cutting tools can all be clamped in place at the same time. They are then brought into use as required without needing to be re-set to centre height see (**Fig. 4**).

Lathe work isn't all done with lathe tools. We have already used a centre drill and a selection of twist drills, not to mention a countersink. But before we got that far we had to get our sizes right and we did that with a micrometer. There's no mystery involved in using a micrometer. All it is, when you look closely at it, is a kind of carpenter's cramp with a circular scale fixed on the screw and a datum line scribed on the body. **Fig. 10** shows both imperial and metric micrometers. The screw has 40 threads/in and the circular scale has 25 divisions. When you rotate the screw once, 25 divisions move past the datum. But you have moved the screw forward one thread, or $\frac{1}{40}$ in.

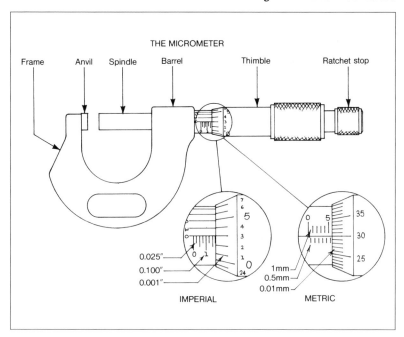

Fig. 10. The micrometer.

Fig. 11. A graph showing spindle speed plotted against work diameter.

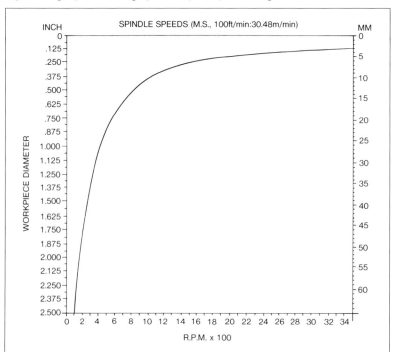

Suppose you only turn the screw one division, (1/25 of a revolution) then it will move toward 1/25 of 1/40 in, which works out at 1/1000 in ('one thou'). If you practice measuring known thicknesses and diameters, such as twist drills and silver steel, you'll soon get the hang of it.

There are one or two other things you will need in addition to those classified as lathe tools. For instance, we'll be centre-drilling and drilling deep holes with twist drills – so we'll need a drill chuck with a Morse Taper (or similar) arbor to fit the socket in the barrel of your tailstock (**Fig. 7**). We prefer to use a simple end-mill holder for our centre drills as it ensures minimum overhang from the tailstock body. Choose your drill-chuck carefully. The more accurate it is the less remedial work you'll have to do on jobs which should have been drilled 'dead centre'. The countersink, which you used to chamfer the corners of the bore in your toolmaker's button is not your ordinary 'rose' bit. The one we would like you to use is about 5/8 in max diameter and has a single deep flute (**Fig. 8**). The first time you use one you'll agree with us, we're sure, that it does a superb job.

Each metal has its own ideal cutting speed and BMS cuts best at between 80 and 100 ft/min surface speed using HSS tools. The graph (**Fig. 11** with both imperial and metric figures) shows the relationship of RPM to diameter of a BMS workpiece, based on a surface speed of 100 ft/min. To complicate matters, the ideal surface speed varies for different materials. **Fig. 12** shows appropriate surface speeds for cutting a selection of common metals. Here's a quick way to work out what spindle speed you need for any particular job.

Cutting speed (ft/min) ÷ 1/4 of work diameter (inches) = RPM. A good rule of thumb method for metric measure is: RPM = 1000S ÷ 3d, where 'S' = Cutting speed (m/min) and 'd' = diameter of workpiece (mm).

You know what metal you're using, so you can check its ideal

Fig. 12. A table of cutting speeds for common metals.

TABLE OF CUTTING SPEEDS
(Using High Speed Steel Tools)

Material	Cutting speed	
	ft/min	m/min
Cast Iron	70	21.3
Wrought Iron	80	24.4
Mild Steel	100	30.5
High Carbon Steel	60	18.3
Stainless Steel	50	15.2
Brass	200	61
Aluminium	300	91.4

cutting speed with **Fig. 12**. You can measure the diameter of the workpiece in inches or millimetres. Get busy with your calculator or pencil and paper and you'll soon come up with the spindle speed you need.

Of course, there's a snag! Lathes have a range of set speeds and, as it's unlikely your lathe will have a speed setting which agrees exactly with the one you've just worked out, you'll have to compromise. Pick the nearest lower speed to your ideal spindle speed. Let us give you an example.

Suppose we want to turn a piece of 1½ in (31.8 mm) dia BMS with HSS (High Speed Steel) Tools. Using our quick formula:

$$\text{Cutting speed} \div \tfrac{1}{4} \text{ work diameter} = \text{RPM}$$
$$100 \div 0.375 = 266$$

On our lathe we have a choice of 200 or 290 rmp. We think, unless the job had some unusual features which made the lower speed more desirable, we would select 290 rpm. If the higher speed had been 350, for example, we would have gone for the 200 rpm option on the grounds that too large a jump upwards in spindle speed was unacceptable. As you read around the subject and gain more experience you'll realise there are other types of lathe tool which allow you to run the spindle faster and take bigger bites, but they are for the future. For now, let's stick to basics. In the next chapter, we'll be doing a different kind of turning in which we don't use a chuck at all. But we will be building on the experience we've gained, as we will throughout the book.

2 BETWEEN-CENTRES PROJECTS

Our next project is to make a plain tapered mandrel which you can later use to mount work for turning the outside diameter concentric with the bore. Because it is going to be used between centres, it must be turned between centres, to make sure the whole outer surface is centred on the axis of the lathe mandrel.

Suppose you had to make a flywheel for a model stationary steam engine and the drawings specified finish turning on its outside diameter and the front and back faces of the rim. With a mandrel of the correct size you could first drill and ream the bore of the flywheel in the chuck, face off the boss, remove it from the chuck and tap it on to the mandrel with a soft-faced hammer until it was tightly gripped. The assembly would then be set up between centres and the outside diameter and faces

Fig. 13. Details of the mandrels and the mandrel press columns.

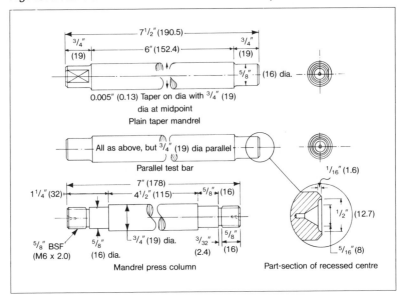

finished. In this way, when the flywheel was assembled to its crankshaft, there would be no trace of wobble when rotated.

Here's how you make your plain tapered mandrel (**Fig. 13**). Cut two pieces of 1 in (25.4 mm) diameter BMS bar 7½ in (190.5 mm) long, at the same time cut two pieces of ¾ in (19 mm) diameter BMS bar 7 in (178 mm) long. When you've prepared them the way we're going to show you, you can put the smaller pieces in a safe place. Those are for the columns on the mandrel press and you'll need them in Chapter 8. Set up one of the larger pieces in the three-jaw chuck. If your lathe has a hole through the mandrel which is big enough to admit ¾ in (19 mm) dia bar, the next job will be much simpler. If you don't, and the bar won't go right into the spindle, you are going to need a fixed steady.

Before we can set up the raw material between centres the ends have to be prepared by facing them off and drilling the ends with a centre drill. This is why we need the three-jaw chuck for the first operation. If you can chuck the bar with only ½ in (12.7 mm) or so protruding from the jaws all well and good. If not, and you have 6 in (152.4 mm) or so of bar sticking out, you need the assistance of a fixed steady on the bed shears (**Fig. 14**). To use the steady, chuck the bar and adjust its setting and

Fig. 14. Use of the fixed steady to support work while recessing one end with a boring tool. Note the 'clog heel' type of toolpost.

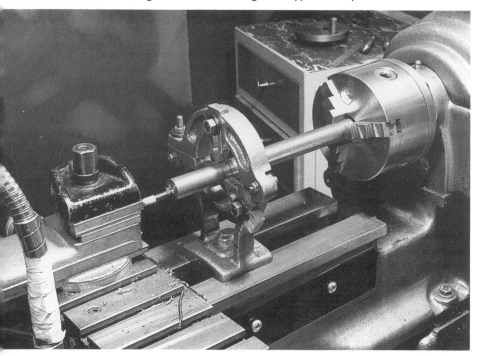

tightness in the chuck until there is no visible wobble when you run the lathe under power. Bring the steady up to the end of the bar and position it so that you have room to get the turning tool across the end. Some fixed steadies have a hinged top which lifts out of the way and can be fastened over the bar when you have it in the right position. Whatever type you use, when the steady is bolted down the three fingers can be adjusted so that they just touch the bar without undue pressure. Turn the mandrel by hand to make sure the bar is not being gripped, but merely supported. Put a squirt of lubricating oil near where the fingers of the steady run on the bar and you are ready to go.

With the lathe set at the right speed for the size of bar, and a turning-and-facing tool in the toolpost, face off the end of the first bar. Try to set the height of your facing tool so that it doesn't leave a 'pip' in the centre of the bar. If it does, adjust the height until it leaves a smooth face right across. When the face is as smooth as you would like, put a No. 4 centre drill in the tailstock chuck and make a full depth centre hole in the bar. By this we mean feed the centre drill in until it begins to cut a parallel hole the size of its body diameter. Don't go in too far. A few thousandths of an inch of the shoulder showing will do, as we are now going to recess the centre hole. Take out the centre drill or protect it with plastic tube, as for the lathe tools. Recessing is a safety precaution to extend the useful life of your mandrel by preventing the 60° socket from getting bruised in workshop use. If this happened the lathe centres might not locate the mandrel correctly next time you tried to use it. To recess the end of the mandrel you will need to replace your turning and facing tool with a small boring tool. When you've done this and set it up to centre height, before you start check that the fingers of the fixed steady are not in need of more oil or closer adjustment. Before we rush on, we should remind you that the boring tool shank should be aligned *parallel* with the bed shears, not at right angles to them as with the turning and facing tool.

Now bring up the point of the boring tool until you can take a light cut which begins inside the centre hole and moves outwards. Position the tool point in the middle of the centre hole. (As near as you can) and zero the cross slide. We want the recess to be ½ in (12.7 mm) dia which means we feed the tool *towards* us for a distance of ¼ in (6.4 mm) reading backwards on the cross slide thimble.

Another way of doing the end-preparation would be to face and centre-drill all four lengths of bar before switching to the boring tool to do the recessing. Whether this would, in fact, save time and trouble we'll leave you to decide.

The recess should be about ¹⁄₁₆ in (1.6 mm) deep when finished, so at least two cuts will be needed. The boring tool is controlled by both the top slide and the cross slide handwheels, a technique which comes quickly with practice. For fine work, such as this recessing, we would advise clamping the saddle as we did for facing the toolmakers' buttons. In this way you can be sure the saddle won't move during the infeed and leave a conical surface on the work. When the recess is finished you can release the bar from the steady, turn it end-for-end in the chuck, re-set the fixed steady fingers and carry out exactly the same operations on the other end. In the unlikely event of anything going wrong and the bar end being spoilt, face it off and start again. The lengths shown on the drawing are not critical in this instance and you have plenty of bar to go at! Set up the other pieces of bar and prepare their ends in the same way, except that only the ends of the mandrel and the test bar need to be recessed. The ends of the press pillars will not need to be protected and can later be rounded off. Consequently, the centre holes in the pillars need only be half the depth of our earlier ones.

With both ends of the bar centred and recessed you can take off the three-jaw chuck, park it in a safe place (complete with its key). Put on the catch plate – a sort of little faceplate with a slot, which goes out to the rim, and a peg sticking out of it. This is what we need to make our 'between-centres' set-up work. Screw the catchplate firmly on to the spindle nose.

Find the two 60° centres which should have come with the

Fig. 15. The lathe set up for turning between centres.

lathe. One goes into the socket in the headstock mandrel and the other into the tailstock barrel. The ideal arrangement, in our view, is to have a solid centre in the headstock and a 'running' centre in the tailstock. Running (or rotating) centres are not expensive as long as you don't demand super accuracy. At our stage of the game, and on this particular project, an inexpensive running centre would be a good buy. If you decide not to use a running centre you'll have to remember to keep checking the tailstock centre for overheating and readjust it as required during the work we're going to do on the mandrel blank. For the moment, we're assuming you have a running centre which needs no lubrication or adjustment unless you take heavy cuts which are likely to cause the bar to heat up. Check it occasionally, anyway.

Pick out a suitable carrier which should be slipped loosely over the headstock end of the bar. Fiddle the carrier about on the end of the bar until its tail is in the right position to hit the catchplate peg. If persistent clicking noises bother you, you'd better tie the carrier tail to the peg or hold it there with a heavy-duty rubber band. Tighten the setscrew until the carrier is held firmly to the bar while you rotate the lathe mandrel. The whole set-up should now look like **Fig. 15**. Return the turning and facing tool to the working position, set to exactly centre height with the correct cutting angle and clamp it up. Check that the lathe is set at the right speed and that you have an auto-feed of no more than 0.0035 in (0.089 mm) per rev selected. Rack the saddle to the right until the tool point is clear of the right hand end of the bar, wind in the tool with the cross slide feed handle and take a cut deep enough to clean up the entire outer surface of the bar, using coolant where possible. Do not take off more than you need to clean up the bar. Measure the diameter with your micrometer or vernier at several places along the length and make a written note of the readings. What we usually do is to make a little sketch of the component we're working on and write the micrometer readings in the places on the sketch where the measurements were made.

You will be very lucky indeed if you find that the sizes are the same at each of the points measured. You are more likely to find the bar tapering if only by a couple of thou (0.05 mm). For the current project this may be just what we're looking for. You will remember what we said earlier about tapping the mandrel into the bore of the flywheel. The reasons we can do that and still have the rim in the correct relationship to the bore is that the mandrel is ever-so-slightly tapered. The taper – in this case 0.005 in (0.13 mm) in the diameter over a length of 6 in (152.4 mm) is sufficient to grip the bore of the workpiece without our losing concentricity. On the other hand the workpiece will move quite a way along the mandrel before it grips hard enough. We have to arrange things so that when the workpiece grips hard, it ends up just about in the centre of the mandrel's length. In other words we have to get the nominal diameter, ¾ in (19 mm), about 3 in (76.2 mm) from one end. It doesn't matter, in this case, which way the bar tapers because we can enter it into a bore either way round. However, tradition decrees that the larger diameter should be at the headstock end.

If the bar only tapers, say, 0.003 in (0.08 mm) along its length we're going to have to do something to increase that taper. If we don't we may find that workpieces move too far before they bind on the mandrel.

But let's get back to turning the diameter. To change the amount of taper over the length of a workpiece we have to move the tailstock centre in relation to the 'live' or headstock centre. **Fig. 16** shows you what this does in practice. The axis of the workpiece moves at one end, but the path of the saddle along the bed shears does not change. If we move the tailstock centre towards the front of the saddle, more metal will be removed at that end than at the headstock end. If we move the tailstock centre towards the back of the lathe, less metal will be removed at the tailstock end.

Find out from your sketch which end of the bar needs to be smaller and get ready to move the tailstock centre the required amount. The simplest and most precise way of doing this is to use a Dial Test Indicator (DTI).

Although a DTI is not cheap, (what tools of quality are cheap these days?) we believe it to be an essential item in a serious machinist's toolkit. If you can find any way of affording one – grab it with both hands. There are several types of DTI, each designed for a specific job. The type we favour has a long plunger travel and can be used for direct measurement, but more about that later. There are one or two things to do before we need the DTI. The method of shifting the tailstock body in and out of alignment varies from lathe to lathe and you should read up on your particular machine before you begin. Soak up all the information you can find in the lathe handbook and make

Fig. 16. The effect on centre position of tailstock set-over. Excessive set-over should be avoided.

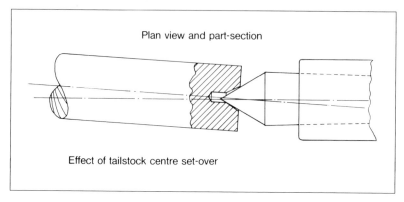

Plan view and part-section

Effect of tailstock centre set-over

Fig. 17. Use of the DTI in setting over the tailstock. The Allen key (bottom right) is to adjust the jack-screws in the tailstock base. Note the 'elephant's foot' tip on the DTI plunger.

sure you know what the procedure is for your machine. It may be different from ours and you'll need to tread carefully, checking each step as you go. We don't want you to get white knuckles gripping the wrench or the allen key, just be prepared to vary the routine to get the right result even when your method seems to be the opposite of ours.

Set up the DTI with its foot against the projecting end of the tailstock barrel (**Fig. 17**) and turn the bezel until the ZERO mark is opposite the needle. This being a precision instrument, measuring very small distances, the needle tends to bounce about a lot until you stop fiddling with it. When the needle has settled down on zero, check again how far you want to move the centre. Say we wanted the workpiece to be 0.004 in (0.10 mm) smaller in diameter at the tailstock end, which means we have to take off 0.002 in (0.05 mm) per side at that end. So the tailstock body needs to be moved towards the front of the lathe a distance of 0.002 in (0.05 mm). The dial of the DTI will probably be graduated in thousandths of an inch (hundredths of a millimetre) and we want to move the needle two divisions. But two divisions in which direction? We can't tell with the naked eye when we're using such small measurements. Look at the face of the DTI again, where the zero mark is. On one side of the zero you will see a plus (+) sign and on the other side a minus (−) sign. Push the plunger up into the body of the instrument and the needle will rotate clockwise. The plus sign will be on the right hand side of the zero mark so that clockwise rotation of the needle is read as a positive (+) figure. Release the plunger and the needle's anticlockwise rotation shows negative (−) movement. To put it another way, if the surface you're testing moves upwards towards the instrument, the needle registers a plus figure, and if the surface falls away from the instrument, the needle registers a minus figure. Believe us – it's all much simpler than it sounds!

Now slacken the screws on the tailstock which need to be slackened, turn the adjusting screws and watch the needle. When it has moved the required amount, in the right direction, tighten everything up again and check that the reading hasn't changed. You may need to do a fair amount of fiddling to get the needle to remain steady, but persevere and you'll achieve your goal. When the needle is at rest in the correct place you can remove the DTI from the lathe shears and take a light cut over the length of the workpiece. Do another sketch and put on it the micrometer readings you take after this cut. You may be delighted to find that the degree of taper is exactly right, in which case you can proceed to the next stage – turning the mandrel to correct diameter at its mid-point. If the taper isn't quite right at this setting, return the DTI to the shears and carry out the procedure as before. Go on adjusting and taking test cuts until you are satisfied with the taper. After that it's just a matter of taking successive cuts until you have the correct ¾ in (19 mm) diameter measured at a point 3 in (76.2 mm) from the tailstock end of the workpiece. Watch out! A small cut off the taper leads to a big movement of the ¾ in diameter along the mandrel.

When you are on the final cut, the one that's going to bring the diameter to the precise size we need, change to a sharpened knife tool. Then, when you take the last couple of cuts, the finish will be so good you'll be tempted to make yourself a whole range of different sized mandrels.

All that needs to be done now is to reduce the diameter at the two ends to ⅝ in (16 mm) and take off the sharp corner with a chamfering tool. But to do this your lathe needs to be reset to turn parallel. Take the taper mandrel you have just made out of the lathe and put it aside.

To re-set the lathe correctly we are going to use the second piece of bar 1 in (25.4 mm) dia and 7½ in (190.5 mm) long, all ready with faced and centred ends. Get it out and set it up between centres. The taper mandrel is finished but the tailstock of the lathe is still displaced. We have to get the tailstock centre back into alignment and, as we do that, we can kill two birds with one stone. We have to establish that the lathe is turning dead parallel again and we do it by reversing the procedure for setting over the tailstock. Put the prepared bar between centres, set up the DTI as before – with needle at zero – and remove the set-over by getting a reading of minus (–) 0.0025 in (0.064 mm). Take a test cut, do a new sketch and note down on it your micrometer measurements. Repeat this process as often as is necessary to get the bar turned dead parallel. When the bar measures up to your expectations, finish the ends by reducing the diameter at the two ends to ⅝ in (16 mm) for a distance of ¾ in (19 mm) and take off the sharp corner with a chamfering tool. If you are using a carbide tip tool here, do not use coolant. The diameter and length are not critical, but the finished test bar will look better if you put a good finish on this part and make the chamfers the same at each end. Work at the tailstock end first. To turn the headstock end of the bar, remove it from between centres, take off the carrier, change it over to the end you've just finished and clamp it on again (with a scrap of copper or soft fibre to protect the turned surface). Now return the bar to the lathe, tie on the carrier as before and away you go.

Finish this end in the same way and what do we have here? We have a parallel test bar which we can use to re-set the lathe alignment each time we've set over the tailstock. The procedure for using a test bar is to set it up between centres and run a DTI along the shears (**Fig. 18**) with the plunger tip in contact with the surface of the bar. When you have adjusted the tailstock until you can run the DTI the full length of the test bar without there being any significant deflection of the needle, the lathe should turn parallel. Simple, isn't it? That's another bit of equipment you'll use a lot in the future.

Now return to the taper mandrel to finish off the ends in exactly the same way as we did the ends of the test bar. If you want to make a really professional job of your plain taper mandrel you can file or mill a flat on the reduced portion, at the larger end, so that the screw of the carrier will not slip under power. If you have access to letter and number stamps it would be useful to have the diameter and length of the mandrel stamped on this flat.

Fig. 18. Checking lathe alignment, with a DTI and a parallel test bar between centres.

While we are still in the 'between-centres' mode, there's one more little job we can do, which seems to follow on naturally from what we've been doing. You can get out the remaining prepared pieces of ¾ in (19 mm) dia bar, now, and set one up between centres. Have a good look at **Fig. 13**, which gives you the main sizes, and you'll see that all we have to do is reduce the diameter at the ends and finish out with a square shoulder. Ignore the screw thread for the moment, we'll come back to that when we start serious work on the mandrel press in Chapter 8.

Swing the turning and facing tool out of the way or take it out and replace it with a knife tool (**Fig. 124**) which will cut from right to left. Set this tool as shown in **Fig. 19** so that you can cut right down into the corner without leaving too much of a radius there. We usually begin by marking the length to be reduced on the surface of the bar with a three-square file or a junior hacksaw blade, leaving a little to clean out when we finish the shoulder. A nick about ¼ in (6.4 mm) long will show up quite well when the work is revolving. You may see some lathe operators resting a rule on the work, up against the inner edge of the cut while the work is revolving. This is a dangerous practice and you should avoid it. You have your mark on the work, start up and take a heavyish cut – say 0.030 in (0.76 mm) – using auto feed to give you an advance of 0.0035 in (0.089 mm) per rev, standing by to drop out the auto feed when the tool approaches your mark. Check the diameter of the reduced portion with a micrometer and carry on turning until you reach ⅝ in (16 mm) diameter. When setting your last cut for precise size, run the feed along about 0.1 in (2.54 mm) and stop for measuring. If OK, proceed. If not, make the necessary adjustment and repeat. It's alright to return the tool to starting position with the work still revolving in the early cuts, but stop the lathe before you return the tool on

Fig. 19. Setting a knife tool to cut a square shoulder.

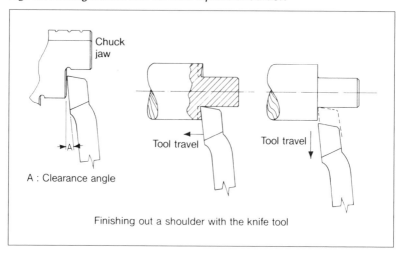

Fig. 20. Measuring the mandrel shoulder length with a digital caliper.

the finishing cut. Otherwise you may end up with an unattractive reverse helix cut on the finished work. Although it's not going to be seen, it is worth cultivating good habits rather than bad ones. Finish the reduced diameter first, then come back to cut the shoulder to the exact length of 1¼ in (32 mm) and finish out the corner. Measure the shoulder length with Vernier or dial calipers (**Fig. 20**).

This is not the place to go into vernier theory, so we'll just give you the facts. A Vernier caliper has two scales: one is fixed to the frame, the other to the sliding jaw (see **Fig. 21**) and you get your reading from the relative positions of marks on these scales. Say we took a length of six tenths of an inch on the fixed scale and made our vernier on the moving scale the same length. The upper scale would contain 24 divisions, each measuring 0.025 in. Now suppose we divided the moving scale into 25 graduations. It's not difficult to work out that each of these divisions would have a length of 0.024 in, and going on from there, that the divisions on the two scales differ by 0.001 in each. So if we put the zero mark of the two scales together and move the sliding scale until the first vernier division comes opposite the first 'fixed' division we must have moved the sliding jaw 0.001 in. It follows that if we move the sliding scale until its 12th division comes opposite a division on the fixed scale, we must have moved the sliding scale a distance of 12 thousandths of an inch. Reading the vernier goes like this: first add up the reading to the left of the zero point on the sliding scale. Check which division on the sliding scale is opposite one of the fixed scale divisions, note its number and add this number of thousandths to the reading you have already. The total is the measurement between the jaws of your Vernier caliper.

Meanwhile, back at the lathe, turn the bar end-for-end and repeat the sequence of operations on the other end, remembering to check speed and feed. And when that column is completed take it out and turn the other column in the same way, making sure that the shoulders are all the same length. They can be put aside when finished, to await the arrival of Chapter 8. Meanwhile we have to find out what a four-jaw chuck can do.

Fig. 21. The vernier caliper.

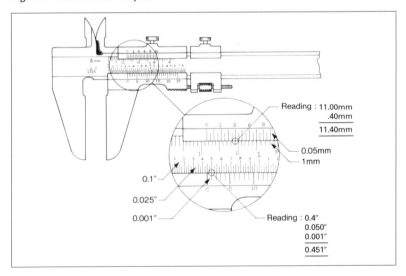

3 *ON AND OFF THE CENTRE*

We were speaking of good habits a moment or two ago. One of the best habits we know – and it applies especially to lathework – is to spend a few minutes thinking about *how* you're going to do a job before you begin cutting metal. This way you don't find yourself having to strip down a set-up that took an hour to devise, simply because you now see a quicker or better way to do it. Get into the habit of sketching ideas – thinking with the pencil – and always keep some scrap paper handy where you keep your measuring and marking out tools. We'll have some practice at thinking out the job later. Now we must take out the centres, take off the catchplate, put on the four-jaw independent

Fig. 22. Left to right: a centring point, toolmaker's buttons with screws and washers, a small boring tool.

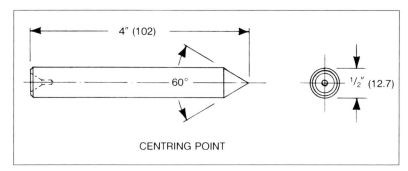

Fig. 23. The centring point.

chuck (**Fig. 24**) and push the tailstock back out of our way.

The next job is not going to tax you too much, because all you're going to do is put a sharp point on a piece of bar. The thing we're going to make next doesn't, as far as we know, have an official title. Let's call it a centring point, and we'll be putting it into service before we get to the end of this chapter. Cut a piece of ½ in (12.7 mm) dia silver steel about 4 in (102 mm) long and set it, roughly central, in the jaws of the four-jaw independent chuck with about 1 in (25.4 mm) protruding. (You'll be surprised how close you can get a bar to running 'true' by eye alone.) To forestall your next two questions – silver steel is a high carbon steel which you usually buy in 13 in (330 mm) lengths and which has special properties for our purposes. The four jaw independent chuck has jaws which you move separately, not all in unison like the three-jaw SC chuck. We'll go into these points in more detail as we get on. Set up the DTI with its plunger positioned so that the tip rests on the top surface of the bar, over the centre line. (**Fig. 24**) and make sure the needle is registering movement throughout one revolution of the bar. It's not important to set the dial to zero in this case because we're not measuring distances, we're watching for the total indicator reading (TIR). Turn the chuck slowly by hand and watch the needle. Remember the plus and minus marks? When the needle moves in the plus direction the top of the bar is rising. When the needle slows, stops and begins to move in the minus direction the top of the bar is falling. The highest plus reading on the dial tells you that the bar needs moving downwards in the chuck at that point. This next bit may sound contradictory, but when you do it you'll see what we mean. Turn the chuck until the 'high' jaw is at the bottom, away from the DTI and slacken the top jaw a little. Now roll the chuck until the 'high' jaw is back at the top and tighten it down. Don't touch the other two jaws at this stage.

Check the rotation again with the DTI and you should see some improvement. The gross swings of the needle should have settled down to a calmer swing from maximum to minimum. Keep on repeating the slackening and tightening routine until you have the needle almost stationary throughout a full revolution of the work. Any remaining tremors of the needle can be removed by giving the chuck key another squeeze on the 'high' side without slackening the opposing jaw. Using a turning and facing tool, face off the end of the bar, checking that the lathe speed is 600 rpm: (If you've forgotten how to do this, look back at Chapter 1.) Centre drill the end, taking in the drill up to its shoulder, to leave a 60° socket about ¼ in (6.4 mm) diameter at the rim. Chamfer the corner, and that's one end of our centring point finished. Did you notice the difference in cutting silver steel when you've been used to using free cutting mild steel? Coolant seems to do more harm than good on silver steel and we don't achieve the polished surface from the tool that BMS consistently gives. We tend to use neat cutting oil (ask your ME suppliers) or nothing at all. But you do need good sharp tools.

Push the tailstock back and remove the centre drill. Take the bar out of the chuck without disturbing the setting of the jaws more than is necessary, and turn it end for end with ¾ in (19 mm) protruding. Tighten up the jaws and repeat the whole process of coarse and fine adjustment until the DTI needle shows no deflection on a full revolution. You should have all this under control by now and the routine will become second nature after a few such projects. When the silver steel is running true, swap the turning and facing tool for a leftward-cutting knife tool, stoned to a keen edge and set *exactly* on centre height. This is most important in any work involving taper turning. In this instance setting dead on centre height ensures that the tool will cut right to the tip of the 60° point (**Fig. 23**). Have you remembered to put plastic pipe over other exposed tools in the toolpost?

Fig. 24. The silver steel blank for the centring point being centred with a DTI in the four-jaw independent chuck.

Fig. 25. The topslide set to cut the 60° point on the centring point.

The drawing states that the point must have an included angle of 60°, which means the sloping sides make angles of 30° with the axis of the bar. We're going to cut the point using the topslide feedscrew, which is normally set parallel with the travel of the saddle along the bed (ie parallel to the lathe's axis). But we want the tool to travel at 30° to that line, so we swing the topslide through an angle of 30°. Check your lathe handbook to find out how to make such an adjustment. Ours has a couple of clamping screws and a graduated ring marked off in degrees. Yours will have something similar; experiment with it until you can get it over to exactly 30° on your scale. Set it so that the tool travels from the back to the front of the carriage (**Fig. 25**) and try the full travel to check that the feed handle doesn't foul anything on the way. When you've done all that you're ready to start cutting.

Keep the lathe speed at 600 rpm, position the toolpoint against the corner of the bar and check that by using cross slide and topslide feeds together you will be able to cut the full length of the point. Don't try to take too much metal off at once; do it in a series of moderate cuts, say 0.005 in (0.13 mm) until the flat at the end of the bar starts to disappear. Stone up the tool and take off the last whisker of metal with a couple of even finer cuts, removing the flat and leaving a sharp point with smooth flanks. Don't be tempted to use a file or emery cloth to 'clean up' the point or you'll endanger the accuracy you've taken so much care to achieve. The essence of this little device is that the centre hole at one end and the 60° point at the other are both concentric with the diameter of the bar. You'll see why this is vital in our next piece of work. Remove the finished centring point from the chuck. When we make the boring tool later in the chapter you'll see how to harden the point for more durability. Before you do anything else, return the topslide to alignment with the lathe axis.

You've had some practice at using a four-jaw, and we've stressed the importance of getting your metal to run true. Now we're purposely going to make it run out of true – what the pundits would call 'eccentrically'. We are going to make a small boring tool and when you get a chance, you can make a holder for it (**Fig. 26**). Cut yourself a piece of ⅜ in (9.5 mm) dia silver steel 4⅜ in (111 mm) long and file one end reasonably flat and square with the bar. Degrease with meths or white spirit, and coat the end with marking blue, set up on a vee block (**Fig. 30** shows the use of the vee block) and scribe a centre line across it. Measure the diameter with a rule and scribe the line as near central as possible. Turn, using a square, measure inwards towards the centre ⅛ in (3.2 mm) from the edge and scribe a short cross-line (**Fig. 26**). Put the bar, marked end upwards, in the vice and lightly centre pop the crossing of the two lines. Check with a magnifying glass that the pop mark is in the correct place. If it isn't, lean the punch over, strike again and check again. When the pop mark is on the spot, make it deep enough to take the tip of the centring point without it slipping out.

Put the marked bar into the four-jaw with about 2⅜ in (60.3 mm) protruding, trying to get the centre pop mark to run

Fig. 26. Details of the small boring tool and a suggested type of holder.

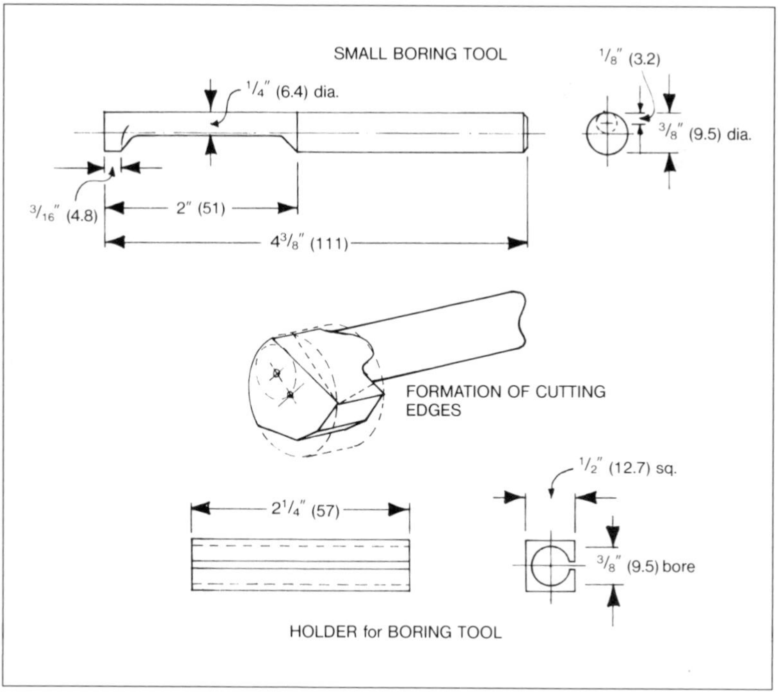

Fig. 27. The centring point and a DTI being used to centre the offset diameter of the small boring tool.

as true as you can by eye. Align the scribed centre line by eye with two of the jaws. Yes, when you run the lathe, the bar will go all over the place, but ignore that and concentrate on the pop mark.

Bring up the tailstock and put in a solid centre. Put the drilled end of your centring point on the centre and adjust it so that its pointed end rests in the pop mark on the workpiece (**Fig. 27**). Don't grip too tightly – just enough to stop it coming loose when you turn the chuck by hand. Set up the DTI with its plunger tip resting on top of the centring point as near the work as it will go. Rotate the work by hand and watch the needle. Keep turning the chuck, adjusting the jaws and watching the needle until it does no more than tremble when you take the work through a complete revolution. At that time, the centre mark on the bar is running true. Take out the centring point, bring up the tailstock centre, enter it into the centre pop mark and we can begin cutting metal.

The ideal tool for this particular job is a round nosed finishing tool (**Fig. 124**) which will give you a good reach and rounded fillets at the end of the turned-down portion of the workpiece. The radius of the tool tip should not be too big – look at the drawing (**Fig. 26**) and use your discretion. If you don't have a round nosed tool use a turning and facing tool set at a suitable angle to cut a reasonably square shoulder. Because the cuts will be intermittent at first, run the lathe at a slower speed than you would for normal turning and take it carefully when you start cutting. The spindle speed is still set at 600 rpm and this will be fine. The indicated speed – from our graph – would be 800 rpm, which we think is too fast for this operation.

Mark the length of the portion to be turned, making one mark ⁹⁄₁₆ in (7 mm) and a second mark 2 in (50.8 mm) from the tailstock end of the workpiece. Be careful when you come to zero the cross slide dial for the first cut. Revolve the work and watch for the place where the surface of the metal comes closest to the toolpoint. Keep the tool well away until you find this position, then touch the tool to the workpiece and zero the thimble. Run the toolpost the full length of the proposed cut to ensure that everything clears the chuck jaws at the end of the travel.

When you have reduced the narrow portion of the work to a diameter of about ¼ in (6.4 mm) clean up the inner shoulders at each end just for appearance's sake and the main turning work is finished (**Fig. 28**).

There are two ways of making these shoulders tidy. You can use the angle facility on the topslide, swinging the slide over at 45° or so and cutting the shoulder neatly at that angle. If you don't want to go to that trouble, you could use the two-handed feed method, which means you have the tool set to clear any obstructions at either end and feed it inwards using both cross-slide and topslide feed handles. It sounds tricky, but you'll be surprised how quickly you learn the knack.

Now roll up your sleeves, you have a spot of delicate filing to do! **Fig. 26** shows you what we are aiming for, a boring tool point which will cut smooth sided bores and square ends to blind holes or steps. With hacksaw and file, remove excess metal checking angles as you work by setting up the shank of your workpiece in a vee block on a flat surface, moving a square

Fig. 28. A round nosed tool in use cleaning up the shoulders of the small boring tool. The topslide has been slightly set over to clear the tailstock body in close-up working.

up to the filed edges and using your eyes. These angles are not critical. Get them as close as you can. Finish off all surfaces with a fine precision file, blending the cutting head neatly into the shank where it needs it, because you won't be able to do any more filing after you've hardened the tip.

Hardening is very simple and you can do small items over a DIY gas blowlamp, although purpose-made Propane equipment would be better for the more ambitious jobs. Check the first aid box before you start, and take all necessary safety precautions. Only heat the tip, with the shank gripped in pliers or a self-grip wrench, and watch its colour – it heats up very rapidly. When the tip reaches bright red, quench it in clean water. After this treatment the tool tip is extremely hard. To make it less brittle and give it toughness, the hardened part should be tempered, but you can do a lot of useful boring with it as it is.

If you do want to temper your boring tool here's what you do. Clean up the tool tip with emery cloth. Heat the bar well away from the tip and watch for colour changes on the cleaned-up bit of the tool. The bright surface of the metal will go yellowish, then straw coloured and if you leave it too long, first brown and then blue. The straw colours are the ones you want. Quench the tool again before the darker colours reach the tip. Now you can stone the front face and the top face, put a small radius on the point and your tool is ready for use.

The shank is still in the 'soft' condition, so you can put the three-jaw SC chuck on the mandrel nose, and face and chamfer the non-cutting end. If you had the topslide swung over, put it back to zero setting now. The finished boring tool can be clamped in the clogheel toolpost or the fourway or you could make the simple holder shown in **Fig. 26**. When you get a minute to spare, make a block of wood with holes in different sizes drilled partway through it. If you keep your boring tools and other special cutting tools upright in this block, they'll be kept apart and they'll last a lot longer and give better service than if you tossed them all together in a drawer.

The job we've just finished was small and fiddly; the next one's going to seem simple and clumsy by comparison (**Fig. 29**). Later, you'll find a drawing of a toggle punch (*Chapter 11*) which is a gadget for punching holes in sheet metal. We're going to make the eccentric for this punch and we'll need a piece of 1¾ in (44.5) dia FCBMS (*see Glossary*) about 3⅛ in (79.4 mm) long. This is twice as long as the drawing says, but we need extra length for chucking. Cutting speed? Look at the **Figs.11** and **12** in Chapter 1. Grip the bar in the three-jaw SC chuck with about 2 in (50.8 mm) protruding and face off the end with a turning and facing tool. Take a cut along the length just deep enough to clean up the surface and put a smooth finish on it, getting as close as you can – in safety – to the chuck jaws. That is all we can do at this setting, so go back to Chapter 1 and remind yourself of the procedure for parting off. Drop the lathe speed to 200 rpm

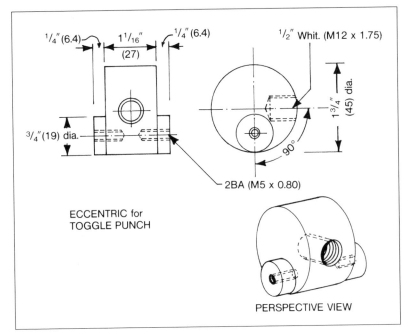

ECCENTRIC for
TOGGLE PUNCH

PERSPECTIVE VIEW

Fig. 29. The eccentric for the toggle punch.

(or similar), change over to a parting-off tool, set at just below centre height, and run coolant right over the cut. Position the tool to cut off a 1⁹⁄₁₆ in (39.7 mm) length of turned bar and, taking it very steadily, part off the workpiece. If you don't have a parting tool long enough to go the full depth, part as far as you can, then saw off the workpiece.

Take the parent bar out of the chuck and put in the newly turned 1⁹⁄₁₆ in (39.7 mm) length with its turned face to the headstock. Face it off as before, remove it from the chuck and measure its length with micrometer or Vernier caliper. When you know the exact length you can put the work back in the chuck and take off the last few thou to bring it to 1⁹⁄₁₆ in (79.7 mm) by bringing up the topslide, and zeroing it on the face of the work. The amount to be removed can be read off the thimble.

You can now remove the three-jaw and put on the four-jaw independent chuck. Leave the lathe for a moment and let's study the drawing (**Fig. 29**) with the workpiece close at hand so that we can visualise what happens next. The eccentric we are going to make will eventually be used to drive the punch in our toggle punch. **Fig. 29** shows it as a solid piece of metal with some parts cut away and some left as they are. Try visualising it as a short fat cylinder with a longer, thinner cylinder passing through it near its circumference with equal amounts sticking out on each side. To get the ends of the thin cylinder in the right place, so

Fig. 30. Scribing centre lines at right angles on the prepared eccentric blank, working on a 12 in × 8 in (304.8 mm × 203.2 mm) surface plate.

that their centre lines coincide, we have to do some careful marking out.

Take off any sharp corners with a file and degrease. Blue both ends of the bar and set it up in a vee-block on a flat surface to scribe a line through its centre. You can do this by clamping a rule upright against an angle plate or a piece of square bar. Using a scribing block (also known as a surface gauge) as shown in **Fig. 30**. First set the scriber point to the lowest edge of the bar's diameter and move the rule until a convenient division coincides with the point. Noting this place on the rule, measure up from it exactly half the diameter of the bar and re-set the scriber point to that measurement. This will be the vertical centre line as shown in **Fig. 29**. Scribe a line across the end of the bar. That is your centre line. Without disturbing the bar scribe a line on the other end. Stand an engineer's square on its stock with the blade pointing up in the air, near your vee-block set up, and sight across it while you slowly turn the bar. When the centre line on the bar end is in line with the blade of the square, scribe a second short centre line to cross the vertical centre line, just as you did with the boring tool. Take the scribing block round to the back of the bar and do the same there. Blue a little of the curved surface and carry this line along one side. Don't disturb the vee-block when you change position. Now measure ½ in (12.7 mm), either upwards or downwards – it doesn't matter which – from the new centre line and set the scriber point to that height. Scribe new short centre lines on each end of the bar. Stand the bar on end and scribe a cross line halfway along the length of the line drawn along the curved side. Make a deep centre pop mark at the intersection. Check with a magnifying glass or jeweller's loupe – it is very important to get it central.

Very lightly centre-pop the outer of the centre crossings on each end. Using a small pair of dividers, scribe a circle ¾ in (19 mm) diameter on each of the pop marks. If you've done your setting out carefully these circles should just touch the circumference of the bar. If they do, you can make the pop marks at their centres a little deeper, to receive the tip of the centring point during the next process. If they don't, and the error is too gross to ignore, clean up the ends with emery cloth and start again with the marking blue. Scribe a witness line right round each end ¼ in (6.4 mm) in from the end on the blued section of the curved side. This will indicate the depth of cut needed.

You'll be getting quite expert at this. Set up the bar in the four-jaw chuck and try to get the pop mark and the smaller circle running true by eye. Bring up the tailstock with a solid centre in the socket and use the centring point and DTI to get the circle running dead true. If you don't remember exactly how it's done, go back to the middle of this chapter and read it up. With the smaller circle centre running true, change the turning and facing tool for a left-hand knife tool set at centre height and adjusted to cut a square shoulder and a flat face (**Fig. 31**).

Keep the lathe running slowly, not more than about 200 rpm and take fine cuts at first to establish the exact length of the shoulder. Keep on taking fine and moderate cuts (not more than 0.005 in or 0.13 mm) until you can see the rim of the scribed circle approaching. Take a last cut which doesn't quite take out the circle and measure the small diameter with micrometer or Vernier calipers. When the diameter measures ¾ in (19 mm), clean out the shoulder and remove any surplus metal from the turned face without going any deeper than ¼ in (6.4 mm) below

Fig. 31. Setting the knife tool to cut down to the small diameter on the eccentric. The smaller circle has been set to run true.

the blued surface of the bar. You could put a small chamfer on the edge of the turned-down portion just to neaten it. Check that everything agrees with the drawing, and you can remove the bar from the chuck. Turn it end-for-end, re-set it so that the centre pop mark runs true and carry out the same operations on this end.

You might, at this point, think of drilling the blind tapped holes in the ends of the small diameters. We would advise against it. The chuck was only travelling at 200 rpm for the turning operation and the lack of balance in the chuck and the workpiece wasn't a problem. If we speed up the lathe to 700 rpm or 800 rpm to start drilling, there would be a lot of vibration. Much safer, in our view, to leave the drilling for the moment and do it later in the drill press. We've machined away most of our markings now, so you'll have to blue one of the flat faces and scribe a new centre line from the centre pop mark on the curved face.

Take the workpiece to the drilling machine and grip it in the vice with the pop mark on the curved side upwards. Set it vertical, as we did when we scribed centre lines at right angles to each other. When the square shows the centre line on the flat face to be upright, tighten the vice finally. Grab your centring point and grip it, finger-tight, in the drill chuck. Now the point tells you when your pop mark lies under the axis of the drilling

Fig. 32. Using the drill press chuck to start cutting the ½ in Whitworth thread in the eccentric. The 'tapping handle' was rescued from a scrapped power tool.

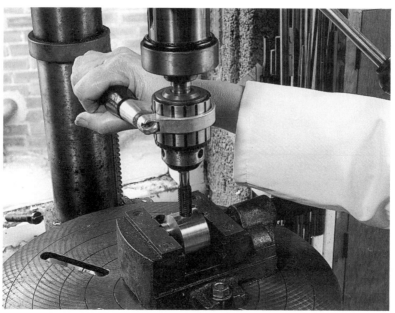

machine spindle. Move the work about until you can drop the centring point tip right into the pop mark, clamp it all down, take out the point and you're ready to start drilling. Starting with a ⅛ in (3.2 mm) or ³⁄₁₆ in (4.8 mm) drill take a hole down to ⅝ in (16 mm) deep, using cutting oil and clearing the chips frequently.

Open out the hole with a ⅜ in (9.5 mm) drill and finish out with the correct tapping drill. For a ½ in (Whitworth thread this would be 0.413 in or 10.5 mm (10.2 mm drill for M12 × 1.7 mm thread). To ensure that the tap cuts a thread which is parallel with the sides of the hole (you won't believe how easy it is not to), we would use the drilling machine chuck to start it off (**Fig. 32**). Here's how you do it. First, take off the belt which drives the spindle, and grip the taper tap, by as much of its shank as possible, in the drill chuck. Wind the chuck down until the tap enters the top of the drilled hole and hold it there while you turn the chuck with the chuck key to cut the first few threads. It's a little different from using a tap wrench, but you'll get used to it. If you can get the taper tap to the bottom of the hole, that will be ideal, but just a few threads can make all the difference. Swap the eccentric around in the vice and drill, and begin tapping the holes in the smaller cylinders.

After all the starting threads are cut, remove the workpiece to the bench vice and complete the tapping of the holes with the correct size tap wrenches. The big, threaded hole takes the screwed end of the operating handle on our toggle punch, but more of that later. In the next chapter, we're going to make a device to help you cut threads on the ends of shafts.

4 TRAVELLING DIEHOLDER

If we could pass bar material through the lathe mandrel bore we could use a die in a travelling dieholder to cut threads. Threading with a die is not as accurate in getting a consistent number of threads to the inch (for *the pitch of a thread, see* **Fig. 69** *in Chapter 8*) as is cutting the thread with a single point tool, but it is quicker and quite accurate enough for most purposes. **Fig. 33** shows a travelling dieholder in use. Now you're going to make one of your own.

Our master plan says 'make the sleeve first and use it as a gauge for the shank diameter' (*see* **Fig. 34** *for more information*). For some jobs it would be more convenient to do it the other way around, but for this one – sleeve first!

Cut yourself a 6 in (152.4 mm) length of 1⅜ in (35 mm) dia BMS bar and grip it in the three-jaw SC chuck with about 3½ in (89 mm) projecting. Set your lathe speed at 300 rpm. With a T&F (turning and facing) tool, face off the end. With so much material overhanging, you should centre-drill the end before going on to do any turning. Then you can bring up the tailstock with a running centre to support the outer end of the work. Mark off a

Fig. 33. The travelling dieholder in use.

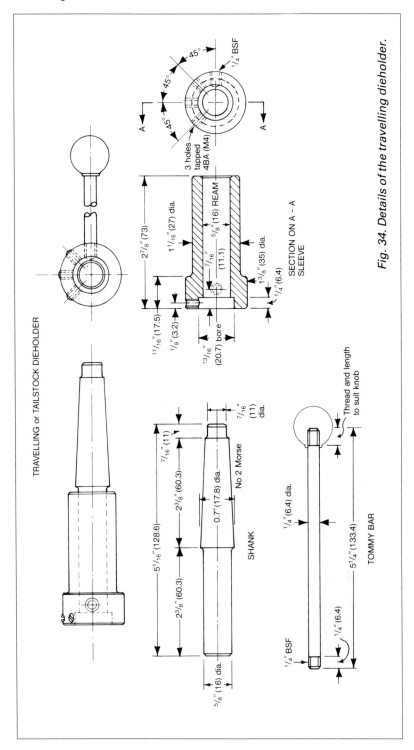

Fig. 34. Details of the travelling dieholder.

length of 2⅛ in (54 mm) on the uncut surface of the bar, with saw or file, and turn down the diameter to 1¹⁄₁₆ in (27 mm) for the marked length. Neither the length nor the diameter are critical dimensions but get as close as you can because it's all good practice in working to a size. Put a good chamfer on the corners of both diameters; never part off with the tailstock centre in position. Move it well away from the work so that the parted-off portion can fall clear.

Change over to a ⅛ in (3.2 mm) wide parting tool, set it as before, ensuring a clearance on both sides of the cutting edge (**Fig. 8**) and drop the spindle speed to about 200 rpm. Position the tool 2⅞ in (73 mm) from the face of the smaller diameter, flood the groove with coolant as you carefully feed in the tool, until the sleeve blank drops into the swarf. STOP the lathe before picking up the workpiece. Before you start parting off, check that the cutting section of your parting tool is long enough to complete the cut. If not, you'll have to go as far as you can and finish off with the hacksaw. Wrap the freshly turned surface in paper or shim and grip it in the three-jaw with the shoulder of the larger diameter just clear of the jaws. Face off with a spindle speed of 600 rpm. Follow the procedure (*Chapter 1*) for drilling a hole through the length of the workpiece. Centre drill first,

Fig. 35. Some reamer types. A: Taper shank, machine reamers; B: Chucking reamers; C: Hand reamers.

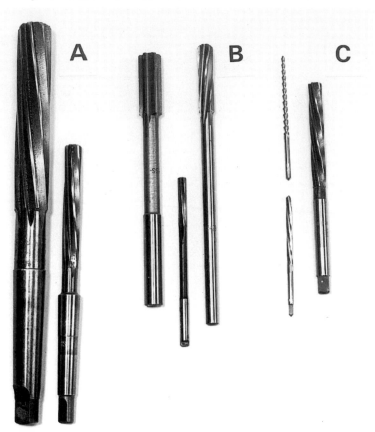

followed by a small diameter drill (⅛ in or 3.2 mm, ³⁄₁₆ in or 9.5 mm) and opening up the hole with, say ⁵⁄₁₆ in (8 mm), ⅜ in (9.5 mm) and finally ³⁹⁄₆₄ in (15.5 mm) drills. Drop the lathe speed for the larger drills. The larger the final drill, the less metal will be left to be removed by the next tool – the reamer.

The purpose of the reamer, which has a lot of sharp, spiral cutting edges along its length, is to turn the roughly drilled hole into a smooth bore of the required diameter. Its function is not to scoop out lots of metal, that's what drills are designed to do. The reamer takes off a small amount and cuts a parallel bore with smooth sides that follow exactly the line of the drilled hole. If you want your reamed bore to be accurate, take care to drill an accurate hole to begin with. Don't force the drills, particularly the smaller ones, or they'll start to wander. The later drills have to follow the path of the first one through, and the reamer follows the path of the last drill. The only way to correct a misaligned hole is to run a long-stemmed boring tool through it, and we don't want to resort to that kind of behaviour just yet.

Fig. 35 shows a few of the kinds of reamer you're likely to see in the catalogues. The most-used ones in home workshops are the hand reamers and the taper shank machine reamers. Chucking reamers are good if you need to ream right to the bottom of a blind hole. We'd suggest using a ⅝ in (16 mm) dia taper shank machine reamer for the bore of your sleeve (these are rather expensive new, so try to get a good used one but check it for sharpness and accidental damage). Take the drill chuck out and slip the reamer shank into the tailstock socket. Change down to about 100 rpm spindle speed and feed the reamer in *and out* very slowly, flooding it with coolant and clearing the swarf frequently. When the reamer passes right through the bore and you can see that the wall is smooth all the way, withdraw it and push the tailstock back out of the way. Take out the reamer and place it in its box or drawer. *DON'T* toss it down on the bench among the filings and the grit.

Swap the parting tool for the T&F tool, checking the point for sharpness and stoning it if it needs it. Skim the 1⅜ in (35 mm) diameter but don't take it down below about 1⁵⁄₁₆ in (33.3 mm), and chamfer the outer corner. Now you'll need your small boring tool to make the socket that the die fits into. Let's see what a die looks like, first (**Fig. 36**). The ones we'll use are called button dies or split circular dies, depending on whose catalogue you use. Hexagonal solid die nuts (**Fig. 36**) are only intended for cleaning up rusty or damaged threads and should not be used to cut new threads. The split in the button die gives scope for a little adjustment on the diameter of the thread but, for the moment, we won't be taking advantage of it. Our sleeve incorporates the three setscrews you need to make those adjustments.

You can make several sleeves to take different sizes of die. The size we're concerned with first is ¹³⁄₁₆ in (20.6 mm) diam-

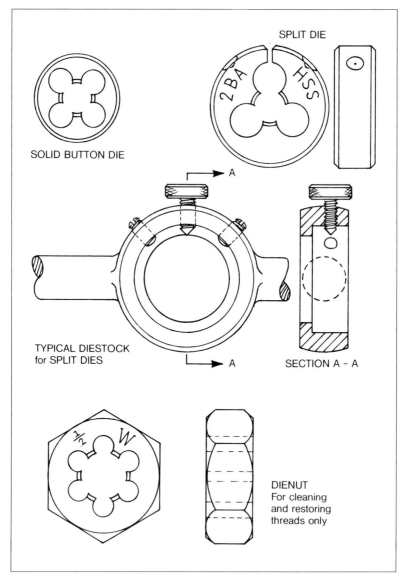

SPLIT DIE

SOLID BUTTON DIE

TYPICAL DIESTOCK
for SPLIT DIES

SECTION A - A

DIENUT
For cleaning
and restoring
threads only

*Fig. 36. A typical diestock and various types of dies. Screws in the
diestock socket engage dimples and a split in the split die.*

eter, with a thickness of ¼ in (6.4 mm). There is a range of sizes
available and within this range there is a number of thread types
and sizes too. It sounds complicated, but it isn't. In practice, you
will find yourself using quite a limited range of threads. After a
few weeks work you will be selecting the right die like a veteran.
Put your boring tool into the toolpost and set it at exactly centre
height, having checked the point for sharpness. If you're not
using the one you made yourself, check that the one you are

using will cut into a corner and leave a flat bottom in the bore
(**Fig. 124**). Some boring tools are only intended to cut through
open bores.

We find that putting a pencil ring on the face to show the
finished diameter is a big help, but be careful using a pencil
while the lathe is running. Rest the pencil on the toolpost,
keeping your fingers well away from the chuck and the tools. It's
only a rough indication, but it will give you a goal to aim at while
you're taking cut after cut. Bring up the carriage to a convenient
place and clamp it to the bed. Wind in the tool point with the
topslide feed handle until it touches the front face, and zero the
thimble. Wind in the cross-slide until the tip of the tool is clear of
the face and will enter the bore. Put on a 0.010 in (0.25 mm) cut
with the topslide feed handle and bring the tool up until it
almost touches the inside of the bore. *STOP there*! What did you
notice? You had to turn the cross-slide feed handle the opposite
way. When you're taking a cut off the outside diameter of a
piece of work you turn the cross-slide handle clockwise and the
tool moves inwards towards the back of the lathe. When you're
taking metal off the inside surface of a bore you turn the
cross-slide handle anticlockwise and the tool moves outwards
towards you. If we seem to be labouring an obvious point,
please forgive us. We're only trying to save you from yourself.
One day you'll forget, when the bore is within a whisker of
finished size, and you'll turn the handle the wrong way. This
may not seem disastrous while we're talking about it here, but it
means you've lost control of the position of the tool point. Now
you'll have to bring it − very gingerly − back to its previous
position and hope against hope you don't take off too much
when the cutting edge makes contact again. We've even gone
so far as to stick a piece of tape, with an arrow drawn on it, just
above the witness line on the cross slide thimble, to make sure
we remembered.

With a firm grip on the cross-slide handle, feed out the tool
until it doesn't quite take out your line. Check to make sure the
recess is not too big in diameter − we'd leave on about 0.020 in
(0.50 mm) for cleaning up when we've reached full depth − and
go on taking cuts until you're nearly there. After you have
established the maximum inside diameter with your first pass,
you could increase the cut to 0.030 in (0.76 mm) or more if you
think the tool is up to it. You'll be able to tell by its deflection
whether you are trying to get on too fast. The depth of the recess
can be read off the topslide thimble. It needs to be ¼ in (6.4 mm)
deep. When you have reached correct depth it's time to finish
out the bore to ¹³⁄₁₆ in (20.7 mm)

Unlock the saddle for this part of the operation, and leave the
topslide where it is. Further cuts off the inside of the bore will be
made with the saddle handwheel and the cross-slide feed.
(Using autofeed for a travel of only ¼ in (6.4 mm) is not really
practical.) Put a fine cut on, with the tool almost level with the

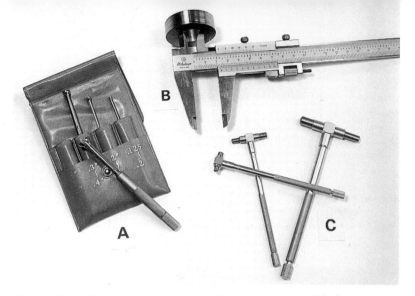

Fig. 37. Some instruments for measuring bores. A: small hole gauges; B: the internal jaws of the Vernier caliper; C: telescoping gauges.

face, and gently rack it into the bore with the saddle handwheel. You could also carry out this operation with the saddle clamped, using the topslide handle. Move the tool back, out of the way so that you can measure the bore of the recess. 'But what do we measure it with?' you may cry. **Fig. 37** should enlighten you, as it shows one or two different instruments for measuring inside diameters. We won't go into detail here, we'll come back to this when we're finishing the sleeve. For now, suppose you only have a digital caliper and we're going to check the size with that. Close the inside jaws of the caliper until it enters the recess, then open it up gently with the thumb wheel until it contacts the diameter with no wobble. When it reaches a maximum figure, read the size off the display and note it down on your pad. Calculate how much metal has to come off *each side* and put it on the necessary cut with the cross-slide feed handle. (Remember – anticlockwise). Stone the point of the tool and take the cut. If you have a die handy, you can try it in the recess and make any slight adjustments that might be needed, but don't take the sleeve out of the chuck just yet. Degrease and blue the face and the large diameter.

Let's discuss how to measure inside bores. Inside micrometers are only any good for measuring holes of 1 in (25.4 mm) or more. Most of the bore-measuring we're going to do will fall well below that limit. Although there are telescoping gauges which will measure larger bores, the sets of gauges usually go down to about $\frac{5}{16}$ in (8 mm). The telescoping gauge doesn't measure directly, its setting has to be checked with a micrometer or caliper (**Fig. 38**). The small hole gauge, too, is set to the bore, and then the setting is checked with a micrometer. Neither of these aids is easy to use. It takes practice to get the 'feel' of the correct setting. The most direct reading instrument is the digital caliper. Once the internal jaws are settled in the

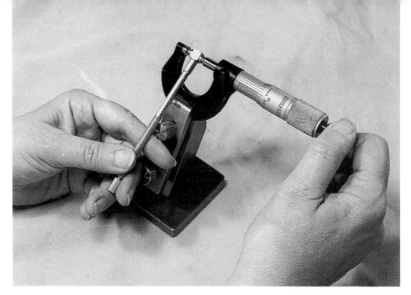

Fig. 38. Checking the setting of the telescoping gauge with a micrometer held in a simple bench stand.

bore, the maximum reading is easily found. Home-made plug gauges are useful for working by the 'cut-and-try' system. We're going to do that on the next workpiece, but now we have to finish off the sleeve by marking out the positions of the three tapped holes and the blind tapped hole for the tommy bar (**Fig. 34**).

The method we recommend, at this stage in the game, is a very simple one. If the holes had to be positioned with great accuracy this method wouldn't work, but it will suit our purposes admirably. Cut a strip of paper ⅜ in (9.5 mm) wide and just long enough to go round the large diameter of the sleeve

Fig. 39. The paper-strip method of dividing for the screw holes.

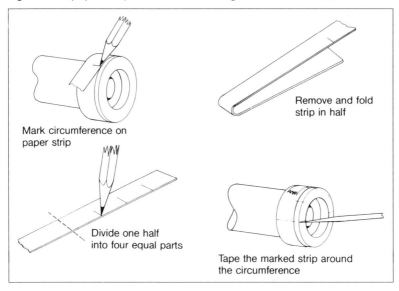

Mark circumference on paper strip

Remove and fold strip in half

Divide one half into four equal parts

Tape the marked strip around the circumference

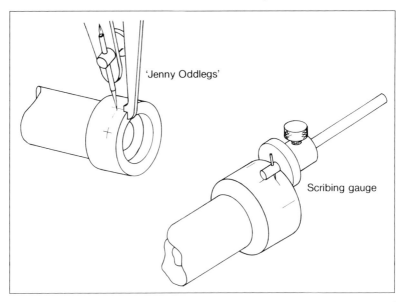

Fig. 40. Alternative ways of scribing the centre lines around the rim of the sleeve, with 'Jenny Oddlegs' and with a scribing gauge.

with only a tiny amount of overlap (**Fig. 39**). Put a pencil mark where the paper overlaps, remove it from the job and spread it flat on the bench. Now study the way the four holes are set out on the drawing. Their centres are at 45° to each other and, if there was a fifth hole opposite the tommy bar hole, they'd divide the upper half of the circle into four equal parts. So, divide your piece of paper into halves, either by folding or by measurement, and then divide one of the halves into four equal parts. Put clear pencil marks across the strip, to show where the divisions come, and fasten it back around the work with adhesive tape, pencil marks outwards.

Set the scriber of the surface gauge to centre height from the bed shears, move the chuck by hand until one of the pencil marks comes opposite the scriber point and scribe a line all the way across the face. Do the same for the other three pencil marks, and remove the paper strip. Carefully pick up the position of each line and carry it round along the diameter. Using a pair of oddlegs or a scribing gauge (**Fig. 40**), mark a line ⅛ in (3.2 mm) from the front face to cross the first three lines. For the tommy bar hole you'll need your line ⁷⁄₁₆ in (11.1 mm) back. The intersections of these lines with the longitudinal lines are the centres for the tapped holes. Now you can remove the sleeve from the chuck and spot the centres with a fine pointed centre punch. Set up the sleeve in the drill vice, squaring up the centre lines by eye as before (when we drilled and tapped for the handle on the eccentric in Chapter 3) with an engineers square off the drill press table. Drill the first three (adjacent) holes right

through at 3 mm for 4BA screws (3.3 mm drill for M4 × 0.7).
Drill the fourth hole ¹³⁄₆₄ in (5.2 mm) dia for a depth of ³⁄₁₆ in
(4.8 mm). This is the tapping size for a ¼ in BSF thread (5 mm
drill for M6 × 1 mm). Start all the threads in the drill press and
finish them off in the vice with a tapwrench. *DO* avoid clearing
tapping swarf from the recess with your fingers; use a cocktail
stick or a swarf brush. Be careful not to use too much muscle on
the tapwrench when you're getting near the bottom of the blind
tapped hole. Feel for the extra resistance and stop twisting
when you encounter it. Find three 4BA grub screws about ¼ in
(6.4 mm) long for the through holes and put them in place. We'll
make the tommy bar later, when we've made the shank for our
dieholder, so put the sleeve aside and cut a piece of ¾ in
(19 mm) dia bar 5⅛ in (130.2 mm) long.

Grip the bar in the three-jaw chuck with 2⅝ in (66.7 mm)
projecting, put a T&F tool in the toolpost and set the spindle
speed at 600 rpm. Face the projecting end and mark off a length
of about 2¼ in (57.2mm) along the bar. Touch the tool to the
work and zero the cross-slide feed thimble. Taking cuts of
0.020 in (0.50 mm) or more, reduce the diameter to 0.63 in
(16 mm). Now you'll see what we meant by cut-and-try. Place
the sleeve on the boring table where you can reach it without
risking damage to your fingers. Try the bore over the turned end
of the shank. Keep taking off small amounts of metal, and trying
the sleeve, watching the readings on your cross slide thimble,
until the end of the shank just enters the bore. The kind of fit
we're looking for is called an 'easy sliding fit' which means the
shank must move easily – but not sloppily – inside the sleeve.
All we can say is that you'll know when you've got it; it will feel
just right. The amounts of metal to be removed in the later
stages are very small, probably so small that each cut will be no
more than a fraction of the thickness of one of the graduation
marks on the feed thimble. Your cutting tool must be razor sharp
and your concentration total.

Put the completed sleeve in a safe place, chamfer off the end
of the shank and take it out of the chuck. The three-jaw chuck
can be removed now, a solid centre put into the spindle nose
and a similar centre in the tailstock barrel. (We're not going to
turn between centres, this is just a 'setting-up' operation.) We
need something with a No.2 Morse taper shank and centre holes
at each end. A taper shank reamer would do, but a MT sleeve
(*see Glossary*) would be even better (**Fig. 41**). Nip the sleeve
between the centres with the larger end towards the headstock.
The object of this exercise is to set the topslide at the correct
angle for turning the tapered surface.

If you look closely at the way the topslide is fixed to the
cross-slide (or boring table, as some call it) you will notice a ring
graduated in degrees and a witness mark to which it can be set.
The method of adjusting it may be different on your lathe;
consult your lathe handbook. On our lathe there are two

Fig. 41. Setting the angles of the topslide for cutting a No. 2 Morse taper. A 1 MT to 2 MT drill sleeve is held between centres with the DTI mounted in the toolpost.

grubscrews, buried in the sides of the cross-slide, which have to be slackened to allow the topslide to rotate. When you've released it, swing it back slightly, with its feed handle towards the rear of the lathe. Only tighten it up lightly for the moment. Set your DTI in the toolpost with the plunger pointing towards the work (**Fig. 41**) or, in this case, towards the taper sleeve we're using as a 'master-taper'. The tip of the plunger must be at centre height, and the plunger must be at right angles to the tapered surface of the sleeve. If you didn't meet these requirements you might end up with a false reading and, thus, an inaccurate taper.

Crank the topslide feed handle backwards until the slide won't travel any further without coming off the feed nut. Move the toolpost forward to bring the DTI probe into contact with the smaller end of the sleeve so that it shows some movement of the needle. Zero the bezel of the DTI and slowly wind the toolpost along towards the larger end of the sleeve, keeping your eye on the DTI needle. Tap the sides of the topslide body with a soft-faced hammer or a heavy piece of wood to make the small adjustments needed. Lift the plunger from the surface of the metal while you tap. The topslide is correctly set when the DTI can travel the full length of the taper without the needle showing any sign of movement. At this point, you can finally tighten the holding screws.

Take out the solid centres from the spindle nose and tailstock barrel and put on the four-jaw independent chuck. Wrap paper or shim around the freshly turned part of the shank and grip it in the four-jaw chuck with enough room left in front of the jaws to get a DTI probe on to the turned diameter. Set up the DTI on the bed shears and adjust the chuck jaws until the turned diameter of the workpiece is running true. Move the tailstock out of the way, wind the topslide back to the beginning of its travel (i.e. back towards the tailstock) and advance the tool with the cross-slide feed handle to begin cutting. When you've taken off enough metal to have cleaned up over half the unturned length of the shank it's time to start gauging the taper.

You are unlikely to have access to a No 2 MT ring gauge, which is what the toolmaker would use, but you can easily get hold of a new or used 2-3 MT drill-sleeve. This is the next size up from the 1-2 MT sleeve we used for setting up (*see Glossary*). Very handy things, drill-sleeves! Rack the tool away from the work and try the sleeve over the turned taper. If you smear a little engineers' blue (marking paste) on the taper, the clean marks – where the sleeve has rubbed on the metal – will tell you which part needs attention. Slacken off the topslide holding screws, tap the topslide body with a hammer or mallet in the required direction (*TAP*, mind you, not *clout!*) and re-tighten the screws. Skim a little more metal off, and gauge again with fresh marking paste. Only tiny errors should remain, and before long your taper will fit the gauge perfectly. All that remains to do is to reduce the diameter until the larger end measures no more than 0.7 in (17.8 mm) dia. If you want to be a perfectionist you could relieve the diameter by $\frac{1}{16}$ in (1.6 mm) at the smaller end, for a length of $\frac{5}{16}$ in (8 mm). Chamfer off the sharp corner and your travelling dieholder is finished, except for its tommy bar.

The tommy bar is made of $\frac{1}{4}$ in (6.4 mm) dia BMS 5$\frac{1}{4}$ in (133.4 mm) long. Face off each end in the three-jaw SC chuck and put on good deep chamfers to start the threads. Put the shank of your new dieholder into the tailstock barrel, put a $\frac{1}{4}$ in BSF (M6 × 1 mm) die in the recess and turn the screws only 'finger' tight to hold it in place. Slip the sleeve over the shank and bring the tailstock up until the die is about $\frac{3}{8}$ in (9.5 mm) from the end of the tommy bar. To stop the sleeve turning, wrap it with emery cloth (abrasive inwards) and hold it tightly. Drop the lathe spindle speed to about 60 rpm, in backgear, dose the end of the bar liberally with neat cutting oil and advance the tailstock barrel by handwheel until the die begins to cut. The work will only have to revolve about seven times to cut the length of thread we need, after which the spindle should be stopped, the motor reversed and the die backed clear of the bar. Check the length with a rule and try the thread in the tapped hole of the sleeve.

Now you have a choice. You could leave the protruding end of the tommy bar plain with its chamfered end. It would be serviceable enough, but its looks wouldn't excite you enough for you to dash off three more dieholders. How about screwing the outer end as well, and fitting it with a plastic knob of a suitable colour. How you finish off jobs like this says a lot about how much fun you get out of doing metal work in general. Think about what you want your own customized workshops to be like, and plan accordingly.

5 *SKYHOOKS*

This chapter is about skyhooks. If you didn't know about skyhooks, we'd better explain. There are some jobs in any form of practical pursuit which call for more than the standard issue of a single pair of hands. If you're working in a factory with scores of other willing hands available, no problem. But suppose you have a long workpiece to set up on the drill press table, you know it's going to give you trouble in getting it level, and you're in the workshop on your own. There are two ways you can go about it. You can prop it up on packings of the right shapes and sizes (you'll probably end up with a dozen or so) and

Fig. 42. 'Skyhooks' – a self-grip mole wrench (left) and a roller floor steady.

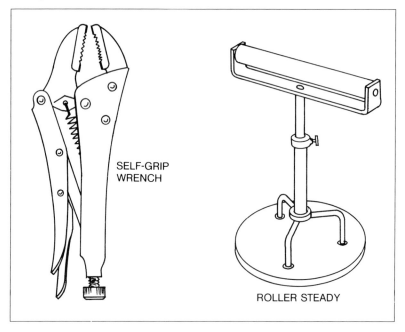

SELF-GRIP
WRENCH

ROLLER STEADY

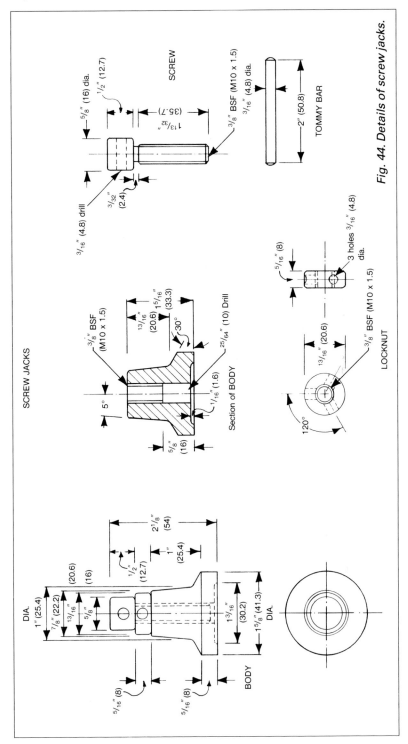

Fig. 44. Details of screw jacks.

Fig. 43. Two screw jacks levelling a milling maching overarm bearing casting. Note the recessed base and the counterbored central hole of the third jack.

hope they don't shift when you start drilling – or you can use skyhooks.

Skyhooks come in many forms: the self-grip wrench is one, and so is the roller floor steady (**Fig. 42**), but the one you're going to make now is known as a screw jack. **Fig. 43** shows a pair of screw jacks in use on a surface plate, but they have many other

Fig. 45. With this amount of overhang from the rotary table (left) the work needs extra support.

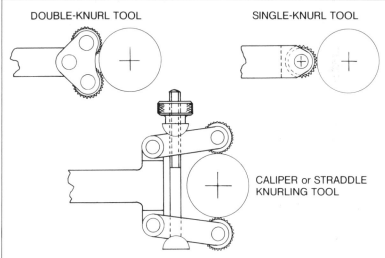

DOUBLE-KNURL TOOL

SINGLE-KNURL TOOL

CALIPER or STRADDLE
KNURLING TOOL

Top *Fig. 46. The 30° tapered skirt being cut on the screw jack body.*

Above *Fig. 47. Some knurling methods.*

uses you'll enjoy discovering. Our screw jack has three parts: a body, a screw and a locknut (**Fig. 44**).

If you're never going to use your screw jacks for anything other than marking out or inspection of finished components, you may feel you don't need the locknut. There won't be enough vibration to loosen and displace the screw, you may think. However, our experience has been revealing. Yes, we told ourselves we'd only use them on the surface table, but then we had to set up a job in a chuck in a rotary table on the milling machine with lots of overhang under the cutter (**Fig. 45**). How were we going to make sure the work wouldn't be pushed down under the cut? There wasn't much space for loose packings, and anyway they'd move when we rotated the set-up to the next station. Screw jacks were the obvious answer.

Now we'll stop lecturing you and let you get on. We would begin with the body, for which you'll need 1⅝ in (41.3 mm) dia bar, 2⅜ in (60.3 mm) long, one piece for each jack. If you're making two or three jacks the best plan is to cut your blanks for all the parts at once, and bring them – in turn – to the same stage of processing. By that, we mean carry out all the taper turning, all the knurling, all the threadcutting and all the cross-drilling on each workpiece before changing the machine set-up. If that's not clear, you will see what we mean as we go along.

We are assuming you will have the topslide set parallel with the lathe axis when we begin. Put on the three-jaw chuck. We need a datum point first – that's a point from which we can gauge other movements of the tool. For this you should put a T&F tool in the toolpost and reduce the diameter of the work-piece to 1 in (25.4 mm) for a length of ¾ in (19 mm) with a neat square shoulder. The corner, where the shoulder meets the reduced diameter, is our datum. Face off the outer end. You can carry out the same operations on all the other 1⅝ in (41.3 mm) diameter blanks at this stage. We try to remember to chalkmark the blanks opposite the No. 1 jaw of our three-jaw chuck, so that they go back into the chuck in the same position.

When the blanks are all reduced and faced, set over the topslide to cut the 30° angle, cut this angle on all the blanks and change the topslide setting to the 5° angle. Caution: this is a 5° angle with the lathe axis, the 30° angle was with the line of travel of the cross slide (at right angles to the lathe axis). Practice will remove any lingering uncertainty (**Fig. 46**). Keep the tool sharp; you want a good finish on the body and a small radius where the two tapers meet. We wouldn't cut a chamfer on the neck of the jack body, breaking the sharp corner with a fine file will be enough. You can either leave the skirt of the body plain, cleaned up with emery cloth, or you can diamond-knurl it. If you're going

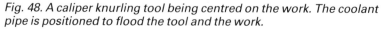

Fig. 48. A caliper knurling tool being centred on the work. The coolant pipe is positioned to flood the tool and the work.

Fig. 49. Tapping with a tapwrench supported on a tailstock centre. Note the paper wrapping to protect the knurled surface.

to knurl, you'll have to do it now, while the embryo body is still attached to the parent blank.

Knurling is another operation, like parting-off, that has a mystique surrounding it which it doesn't deserve. **Fig. 47** shows the two most used methods, and **Fig. 48** shows our own favourite knurling tool in action. The two schools of thought are roughly as follows. Front-approach tools put tremendous side loads on the lathe mandrel, which don't do the bearings a lot of good. Caliper or 'straddle' knurling tools use a combined top and bottom approach in which virtually no side loads are transmitted to the lathe mandrel. The end load, from auto feed, is no more than you get from ordinary turning operations. You've probably guessed that we're caliper-knurling fans and we wouldn't have a front-knurling tool in our workshop at any price.

There are three golden rules: run the lathe slowly (not more than 200 rpm); flood the tool and the workpiece with coolant to wash away the metal powder; and don't try to cut too deeply at one pass. You can traverse the tool with the carriage handwheel – this gives you the 'feel' of the cut – but we prefer to use auto feed at about 0.007 in (0.18 mm) per rev. If you do decide to knurl the skirt of the jack body you may have to slacken the chuck and pull out more of the blank to give you room for the knurling tool's travel. Knurl a length of about ⅜ in (9.5 mm) and you're ready for the next operation, the tapped hole through the centre of the body.

You'll only need reminding of the sequence, at this point in the book. Many of the sub-operations will almost be automatic by now. Centre drill, followed by ⅛ in (3.2 mm) drill, ¼ in (6.4 mm) drill, ²¹/₆₄ in (8.3 mm) drill which is tapping size for ⅜ in BSF (8.35 mm for M10 × 1.5 mm). Take in the 8.3 mm drill

Fig. 50. Tapping with a tap gripped in the tailstock drill-chuck.

to well beyond the limit of the knurled area, to ensure the tapped hole will part off with a full thread. If you don't go far enough you may find the hole hasn't come right through when you part off. The only thing you have not done before is tapping a hole in the lathe. This is done with the lathe in backgear at about 40 rpm. There are two ways you can do it: with a tap wrench supported on a tailstock centre (**Fig. 49**), or with the tap gripped tightly in the tailstock chuck (**Fig. 50**). We favour the tailstock chuck because it gives you a margin for error. If the squared head of the tap is gripped in a tapwrench and the handle of the wrench rests on the bed shears or the cross slide, there is no way the tap is going to 'give' if you suddenly hit the bottom of a blind hole. The tap will probably snap off at the beginning of the flutes before you can stop the lathe. With the tailstock chuck method you can grip the hardened and ground shank of the tap very tightly indeed and still the tap will 'give' (revolve in the chuck jaws) when the tip hits the bottom of the hole. Release the lever clamping the tailstock to the bed when tapping.

After parting off the body, reverse it in the three-jaw chuck, with card or shim to protect the knurling, and change to a boring tool to cut a $\frac{1}{16}$ in (1.6 mm) deep recess $1\frac{3}{16}$ in (30.2 mm) diameter in the base. If the workpiece wobbles a bit when you reverse it, tap it *gently* with a soft faced hammer or a piece of wood until it runs true, then tighten the jaws finally. Open out the lower half of the tapped hole to $\frac{25}{64}$ in (9.9 mm) leaving $\frac{11}{16}$ in (17.5 mm) of thread. Get all your bases to this stage of processing and pick out some $\frac{7}{8}$ in (22.2 mm) dia bar for the locknuts. This material is still a bit big for the mandrel bore of most small lathes but if it will suit yours, you could make two locknuts on each blank. The idea is to turn one end to a certain stage, then reverse the bar in the chuck and work on the other end.

In this way you keep everything at the same setting until all the components are completed. In theory, you cut down the number of short ends of bar you have lying around, but we're not convinced of the savings in practice. When we made the locknuts for the prototype jack, we turned them both on one end of a short piece of bar, tapped them (the same way as we tapped the body), cross-drilled them and chamfered them before parting them off. Think it over – 'Think twice and cut once', as the old cabinet maker said – and do what suits you best.

The only process likely to slow you down is the cross-drilling, for which you will need some method of indexing. Four divisions are quite simple to make, with the bar in vee blocks on a flat surface, an engineer's square and a scribing block (**Fig. 30**). Scribe a horizontal centre line across the face and round the edges of the locknut, rotate it through 90°, checking by eye with the square upright on the surface, and scribe the second centre line as before. Stand the bar on its end to find, and scribe, the centre of the curved surface. Centre pops at the intersections of the lines complete the setting out. But it's not quite so easy for *three* divisions. You could use a 30°/60° set square, or a protractor, to sight the second and third centre lines, but here's an easier way which is just as good.

Don't remove the workpiece from the chuck after the last operation. Blue its outer edge for marking out. You'll need a surface gauge and a short piece of wood, cut so that it holds one of the chuck jaws level when you stand it on the front bed shear (**Fig. 51**). If the piece of wood is hefty enough to stand on the shear without support, it will make the job easier. Set your surface gauge point to centre height, either with a centre height gauge or by checking with a centre in the tailstock. Hold the first chuck jaw hard down on the chunk of wood and scribe a centre line across the face and round the edge of the workpiece (**Fig. 51**). Move the wood to enable you to turn the chuck to the next jaw, hold it down hard on the wood and do the same again. Repeat the whole performance for the third jaw and you have

Fig. 51. A simple dividing method for 120° divisions. Note the protective wood button on the scriber point not in use.

Fig. 52. The tailstock chuck with its jaws retracted, being used to push the diestock while cutting a thread.

three centres as accurately disposed as the jaws of your three-jaw chuck, which is good enough for most practical purposes. 'Why,' you may ask 'do we need the lines across the end face?' This method puts the centres at 120° to each other with reasonable accuracy – what more do we need?

Well, that's fine if you own a toolpost drilling attachment that would let you drill the blind holes in the circumference of the locknuts at centre height without taking the work out of the chuck. But if, like us, you don't have such a treasure, you'll have to remove the work to the drilling vice and position the scribed lines by eye with a square, as before. Take the three ³⁄₁₆ in (4.8 mm) diameter holes carefully into the locknuts. If all has gone well and you now have the locknuts tapped and drilled, with three holes each for their tommy bar, you can chamfer them and part them off. Have a good, critical look at the faces from the parting tool. Do they stand comparison with those faced off before parting? If you don't think they do, take out the parent bar and slip them into the chuck for facing (don't forget shim or card round the outside). Deburr both ends of the tapped hole and the locknuts are finished. For the screws, we need ⅝ in (16 mm) dia bar which will go into the mandrel bore on most small lathes. This means we can work on both ends of one piece of bar, saving a little in setting up time on each operation compared with making parts one at a time.

Grip the bar in your three-jaw chuck with about 2½ in (63.5 mm) projecting and put a sharp knife tool in the toolpost. Set the spindle speed of the lathe at about 700 rpm (smaller diameters need faster speeds) and reduce the diameter of the workpiece to ⅜ in (9.5 mm) for a length of 1½ in (38.1 mm). The tip of this reduced diameter should be given a generous chamfer, because the die we're going to use next will need a good grip on the tip to start cutting properly.

Your travelling dieholder could be used to cut the ⅜ in (or M10) thread, if the die happens to be ¹³/₁₆ in (20.6 mm) outside diameter, but there is another way to do it which is more suitable for the larger sizes of threading dies. This method uses a diestock, but you don't use your hands except to feed in the tailstock barrel (**Fig. 52**). Rack the carriage just far enough back for you to be able to rest the diestock handle on the bed shear when the die is located on the tapered tip of the workpiece. Bring up the tailstock as close as you can and wind it out until either the end of the barrel or the front face of your tailstock chuck is pushing the back of the diestock. This pressure keeps the die at right angles to the axis of the required thread; all you have to do now is revolve the workpiece. But before you go any further, consider that the lathe spindle is set to rotate at 700 rpm – far too fast a speed for thread cutting. You'll need to put the lathe on a much lower speed, using backgear if your lathe doesn't have an all-geared head. We'd suggest a speed of 40 rpm.

Flood the die, and the end of the workpiece, with neat cutting oil or coolant, start the lathe and feed the die on to the work with a firm hand on the tailstock handwheel. This is another of those processes that you pick up very rapidly with practice. Run the die as close as you can to the shoulder and stop the lathe. Clear the swarf away from the holes in the die, wind the tailstock barrel out of your way and reverse the motor. Back the die carefully off the work with a gentle hand on the diestock handle. Let the die clear the end of the thread completely, before you try to take away the diestock. Check the newly cut thread with one of your locknuts. If the fit is a bit on the tight side, no matter,

Fig. 53. Using a parting off tool to recess the thread under the head of a jack screw.

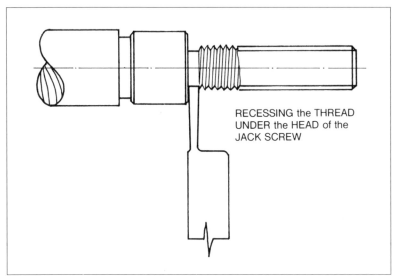

RECESSING the THREAD
UNDER the HEAD of the
JACK SCREW

Fig. 36 in Chapter 4 shows you how to adjust the die to take a little more off. Do be careful when you re-engage the die on the thread or you could find the whole thread removed by the next pass.

Slide the tailstock back out of your way and try to find a small parting tool or, better still, a recessing tool. This is like a parting tool but shorter in the point. Set the recessing tool at centre height and have a good close look at where the thread approaches the shoulder. You will see that the thread peters out to a mere scratch long before it reaches the shoulder. This is because of the taper lead on the inside of the die, affecting the first three or four threads. If we left this alone, we'd have to countersink the locknut to receive the unthreaded portion and in some cases this would be the right thing to do. In our view, seeing a poorly finished end-of-thread everytime you extend the jaw screw is just not on! So our suggestion is that you recess the thread at the head end of the screw (**Fig. 53**).

You can find out what the depth of the thread is supposed to be from tables. You'll find useful tables of this type published as appendices to books, in measuring equipment manufacturers' catalogues and separately, as in the 'Zeus' booklets. Our tables tell us that the depth of a ⅜ in BSF thread should be 0.035 in (0.81 mm) (0.92 mm for M10 × 1.5 mm). We want to cut deeply enough to remove any trace of thread under the head, so we could feed in the recessing tool for a depth of 0.035 in (1.1 mm). Remember this is a direct reading. You don't have to halve it. And that's the hard part done.

Chamfer the top and bottom corners of the head and part off the screw. You know how to mark out, centre pop and drill the cross-hole. It is exactly the same as the other cross-drilling operations we've done together, except that the thread needs protection before you put it in the drilling vice. We've kept the mammoth task until last! The tommy bar is made from a 2 in (50.8 mm) length of ³⁄₁₆ in (4.8 mm) dia BMS bar with its outside diameter cleaned up with emery cloth and both ends rounded with a smooth file.

To use the screw jack, slacken off the locknut, raise the screw to the required height, using the tommy bar if necessary, and re-tighten the locknut. What could be simpler? There is infinite scope for variation on the sizes and shapes we have shown on our drawings. You could make your jacks bigger, smaller, fatter. Make them from hexagonal material to get those interesting conic sections or even make the locknuts from polished brass. There's always a different way to do the job and our words are only suggestions. One of the most important things we're trying to convey to you is the excitement of making something entirely your own. If you can do that, you're not just an engineer but a designer, too! We're going to go for something much more ambitious in the next chapter.

6 *CAT HEAD*

One year, when we were looking for ideas to use in a group of puzzles for Model Engineer, we came across a device called a cat head or cat head chuck. Our first encounter with it was in an American magazine we were reading. We checked it out with several correspondents in the USA and became convinced this was one of those bits of equipment we should own. But what is it used for? Sometimes you need to turn a long thin shaft which is obviously going to spring away from the tool. If it was of bright steel, we could support it in the fixed steady – if it was circular and smooth. But suppose it was rust-damaged, square, hexagonal or had a thread, a flat, a keyway or some splines cut on it – what then? We couldn't use the fingers of the fixed steady in any of these cases, because they must have a smooth circular surface to run on.

Here's where you need your cat head (**Fig. 54**) and you use it

Fig. 54. The cat head in use, preparing the end of a hexagonal bar in the fixed steady.

like this. Put the fixed steady on your lathe with its top open, slip the cat head over the bar and adjust it with the setscrews until the waisted portion runs true and will support the bar where it won't get in the way of subsequent operations. See that there is no springing of the shaft in any direction when you close the steady over the cat head, and adjust the fingers. With both the shaft and the cat head securely supported, lubricate the steady fingers and you are free to turn the end of the shaft. Virtually the same procedure could be used to face and centre drill the ends of awkward long workpieces which could not be passed through the mandrel bore.

Cut yourself a 4¾ in (120.7 mm) length of 1¾ in (44.5 mm) dia BMS bar (1⅜ in [35 mm] of the length is for chucking) and grip it in the three-jaw SC chuck. Push the bar right up to the face of the chuck body before finally tightening the jaws. When you're satisfied with the way it's running, take a skimming cut to clean up the diameter almost up to the chuck jaws. Either a T&F tool or a knife tool will do, as long as it is sharp. Face off the outer end, leaving no 'pip' at the centre.

To reduce the diameter of the waisted portion we made a special round-nose finishing tool (**Fig. 124**) with which we could cut neat shoulders at the ends with a nice radius in the corners. But the vital need, here, is to get the 1⅜ in (35 mm) diameter smooth in both directions – around its circumference and along its length. Whichever tool you choose must be able to do this. We sawed and filed ours from ⅜ in (9.5 mm) square silver steel, and hardened and tempered it just as we did the boring tool and the centring point.

It is one of our fads to get as much done on a workpiece as we can at one setting of the chuck. That's why we changed to a parting tool at this juncture and cut a ³⁄₁₆ in (4.8 mm) deep groove to mark the finished length. (Allowing 20 thou for

Fig. 55. Details of the cat head.

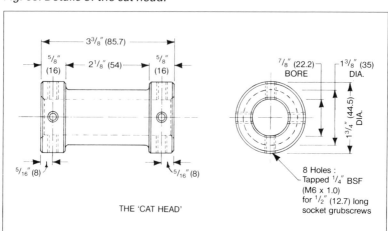

THE 'CAT HEAD'

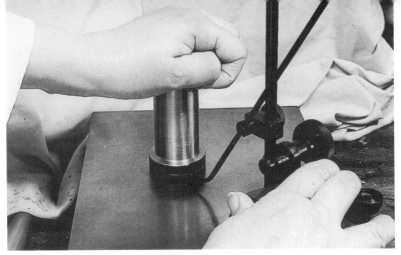

Fig. 56. Scribing centre lines with the surface gauge on a surface plate.

cleaning up, this came out at 3.395 in or 86.2 mm.) Then we were able to chamfer both the outer ends as well as the inner corners of the waisted portion. The outer surfaces are now finished. Put a centre drill in the tailstock, centre drill the end and open it out to 7/8 in (22.2 mm) diameter with two or three drills of increasing sizes, taking in the last drill far enough to clear the parting groove. A drilled finish on this bore will be acceptable. Chamfer the corner of the bore with a small boring tool and part off the cat head body.

After inviting you, several times, to use your initiative in the detail of these projects, we must now weigh in with a caution. If you decide to save material by not adding a chucking piece to your workpiece, remember that your drills will pass right through the blank. Before you start drilling do make sure that the central hole in your three-jaw chuck is big enough to accommodate a 7/8 in (22.2 mm) dia drill. If it isn't, and the big drill cuts into it, this could cost you far more than the material you saved!

Turn the workpiece end-for-end and wrap it with shim or card before re-chucking to skim the second face. Chamfer the corner of the bore and remove the work from the lathe. Degrease and blue the two end faces and the rims of both flanges. Set up the body in a vee block, find its centre with rule, angle plate and surface gauge and scribe centre lines across both faces and along both the flanges. Turn the body through 90° and repeat the operation. To locate the centres of the tapped holes, stand the body on end on a flat surface and set your surface gauge to a height of 5/16 in (8 mm) (**Fig. 56**). Scribe a cross line at every axial line around both flanges and spot them with a small centre punch.

Take the body and its vee block to the drill press, clamp the block to the table with its centre under the axis of the chuck and clamp the body into the vee with a centre line vertical. If your drill table spins and can be swung around the column, it won't be necessary to set the vee block to the drill axis before you

Fig. 57. The drill press table set-up for drilling all eight grubscrew holes at the one setting.

clamp it. Clamp the block to the table first and locate a centre pop mark with the centring point, when you've got the centre line vertical. Lock all movements and check that the body is firmly clamped into the vee block before doing any drilling (**Fig. 57**).

The real advantage of this type of set up is that you can drill all eight of the ⁷⁄₃₂ in (5.6 mm) tapping holes without needing to use the centring point again. Then you can take out the ⁷⁄₃₂ in (5.6 mm) drill, countersink the tapping holes to a good depth, and start all the threads with the ¼ in BSF (M6 × 1.0 mm) tap, also at the same setting. Simply drill a hole, slacken the vee block clamp, roll the body round in its vee until the next pop mark is under the drill or tap and tighten the clamp. Bingo! Ready for drilling (or tapping) again!

With all eight holes drilled and their threads off to a good start, remove the body to the bench vice for finishing off. Then all you have to do is run in eight ½ in (12.7 mm) long, hexagon socket grubscrews with ¼ in (BSF (M6 × 1.0 mm) threads, and your cat head is finished. We have a good reason for specifying grubscrews for this particular job and it has to do with fingers. We like having 10 of them (fingers, not cat heads) so we don't fit hexagon or square-headed setscrews on equipment that rotates at high speeds. The grubscrews will be hidden below the surface of the cat head most of the time, and even when the work almost fills the bore their heads will barely stand proud. Nothing there to whip the end off a finger – or worse! Nevertheless, when you do use your cat head, take the usual extra amount of care to keep your fingers away from all the moving parts.

7 A THIRD HAND

Gadgets that grip the work, so that you can do things to it, are always welcome in the thinking man's workshop. Look at the bolt-down vice in **Fig. 58**. This is an instrument maker's vice, so called for obvious reasons, and if you've never used one, you are in for a treat when yours is finished.

The vice itself is, as you can see, quite small. It has a jaw width of ½ in (12.7 mm) and an opening of ⅞ in (22.2 mm) but it has a few tricks up its sleeve. To start with, it doesn't suffer from lockjaw. That is the difficulty you have with some hinged-jaw instrument maker's vices (**Fig. 60**) when you're working near capacity and round objects won't stay gripped in the jaws.

Ours has jaws that stay roughly parallel all the way out, because it has a guide rod and a good long screw. The vice incorporates a round stalk which you can either insert directly into the neck of the base, or attach to one or both of the knuckles to give you double-jointed movement. You could, if you wished,

Fig. 58. Seated at the woodwork vice, Audrey tries out the completed instrument maker's vice.

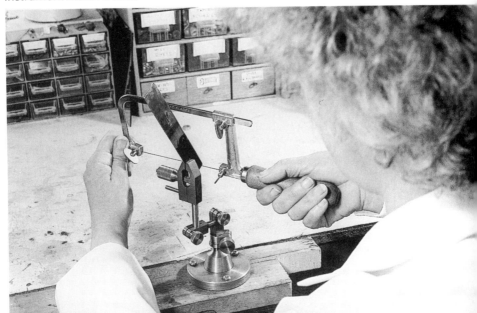

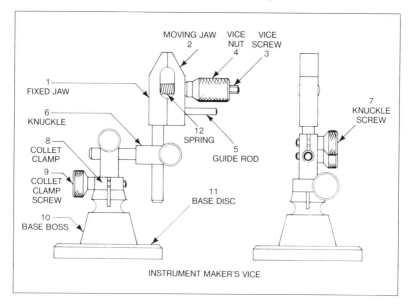

INSTRUMENT MAKER'S VICE

Fig. 59. General arrangement of the instrument maker's vice.

Fig. 60. The unsatisfactory grip of a hinged vice at large jaw-openings.

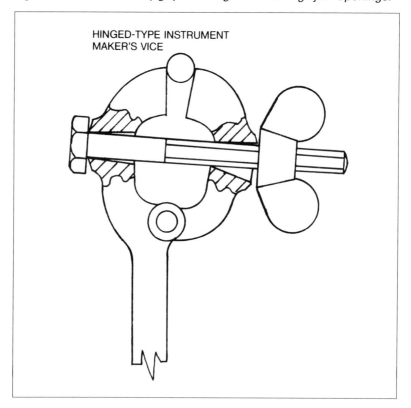

HINGED-TYPE INSTRUMENT
MAKER'S VICE

make yourself an extra knuckle. This would give you extra movement, but by that time your vice jaws would be a fair distance from the axis of the base. The more ideas you toss around, the better you get at picking out the good ones and discarding the not so good.

You will notice that the base isn't carved out of one piece of 3⅛ in (80 mm) dia bar. That would be a bit expensive and rather wasteful of material. Instead, we made ours of 1⅝ in (41.3 mm) 1.575 in) dia BMS (3 in long, or 76.2 mm, for chucking) spigoted on to a ⅜ in (9.5 mm) thick disc of hot rolled plate. Spigoted? That simply means we made a ¾ in (19 mm) hole in the centre of the plate and turned a peg (spigot) the same diameter on the boss.

We put the base boss blank in the three-jaw SC chuck, gripped on the ¾ in (19 mm) extra length, and turned the 15° taper first. We turned down the neck, to 9/16 in (14.3 mm) dia and cut the semicircular groove. We drilled and reamed the 5/16 in (8 mm) hole down the middle, parted down to a diameter of ¾ in (19 mm) by ⅜ in (9.5 mm) wide for the spigot, but then we got nervous. Rather than trying to part the work right off, we decided to play safe – removed the whole thing to our metal bandsaw and sawed off the finished boss. Then we were able to grip the boss by its neck diameter and skim the face of the spigot so that it would not stick out on the other side of the base disc. We degreased the boss and disc, cemented one to the other with anaerobic adhesive, and after the recommended curing time the joint was strong enough for us to mill the four slits with a 1/16 in (1.6 mm) slitting saw. For this operation, you need to take fine cuts and not be too hasty with the feed handle. But you can please yourself whether you saw (or mill) the four slits before or after you assemble the base.

If you already own a radius tool (**Fig. 124**) of suitable size – 3/16 in (4.8 mm) rad is just a guide – you'll have no problem with the semicircular groove. if you don't, you might like to make one from ⅜ in (9.5 mm) square silver steel. Study the clearance angles on **Fig. 124** and when you've sawn and filed it to shape, harden and temper the tip as discussed in Chapter 3. By the way, this groove isn't there just to make the base look good, although it does that too, we think. It is really a deliberately induced point of weakness at the root of the saw cuts. If we didn't weaken this part of the taper there might be too much metal there to let us squeeze the collet tightly on to the stalks of the vice or its knuckles.

The holding-down holes in the base disc are drilled ¼ in (6.4 mm) on a pitch circle of 2½ in (63.5 mm) diameter. The holes will be near enough to their required spacing if you set out the angles with dividers or use the three-jaw chuck jaws and a wooden stop as before and measure inwards 5/16 in (8 mm) from the edge. Two other components are needed to complete the base: the collet clamp and its screw. The collet clamp screw

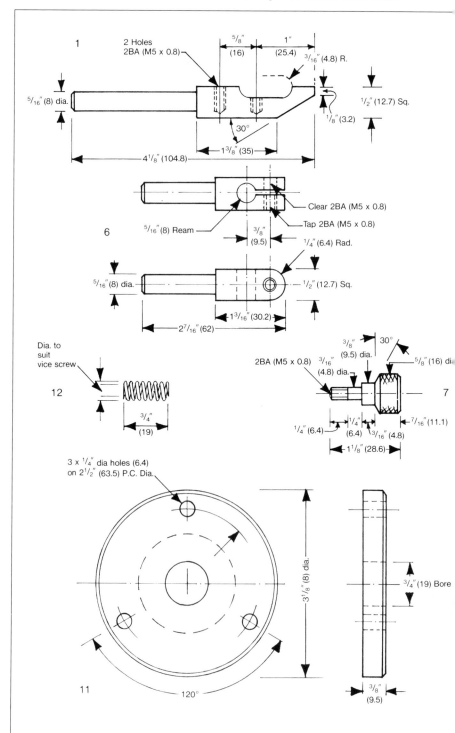

1

2 Holes
2BA (M5 x 0.8)

⁵/₈" (16)

1" (25.4)

³/₁₆" (4.8) R.

⁵/₁₆" (8) dia.

30°

¹/₂" (12.7) Sq.

¹/₈" (3.2)

1³/₈" (35)

4¹/₈" (104.8)

6

⁵/₁₆" (8) Ream

³/₈" (9.5)

Clear 2BA (M5 x 0.8)

Tap 2BA (M5 x 0.8)

¹/₄" (6.4) Rad.

⁵/₁₆" (8) dia.

¹/₂" (12.7) Sq.

1³/₁₆" (30.2)

2⁷/₁₆" (62)

Dia. to
suit
vice screw

12

³/₄" (19)

2BA (M5 x 0.8)

³/₁₆" (4.8) dia.

³/₈" (9.5) dia.

30°

⁵/₈" (16) dia

¹/₄" (6.4)

¹/₄" (6.4)

³/₁₆" (4.8)

⁷/₁₆" (11.1)

1¹/₈" (28.6)

7

3 x ¹/₄" dia holes (6.4)
on 2¹/₂" (63.5) P.C. Dia.

3¹/₈" (8) dia.

³/₄" (19) Bore

11

120°

³/₈" (9.5)

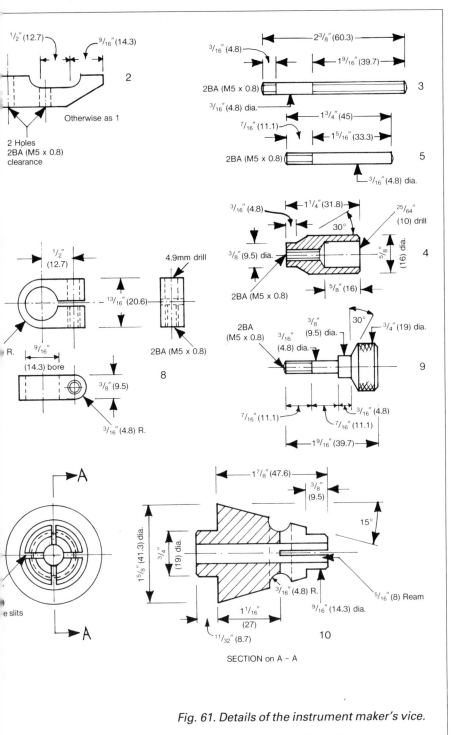

Fig. 61. Details of the instrument maker's vice.

is a straightforward piece of turning, threading and knurling which we won't dwell on. The knuckle screws are similar and can be made at the same time. The collet clamp itself (**Fig. 62**) is a bit fiddly, and it will try your patience. Cut off a piece of 1³/₁₆ in × ³/₈ in (20.6 mm × 9.5 mm) BMS flat, long enough to make the clamp with some metal left to clean up. Brighten the sides and faces, degrease and blue them. Mark out the positions of the ⁹/₁₆ in (14.3 mm) diameter hole and the 2BA (M5 × 0.8 mm) tapping hole on all faces, making light pop-marks at their centres. Scribe the circles for the rounded ends.

The ⁹/₁₆ in (14.3 mm) hole must be drilled or bored to fit snugly (not tightly) over the collet. This can be done in the drill vice, with care, but we would advise you to consider doing it in the four-jaw chuck. Granted, it's more trouble, but the results are much more predictable. The clamp will look a mess if it does not sit square on the shoulder of the collet.

You will remember how you set up the eccentric in the four-jaw chuck, back in Chapter 3. The process is exactly the same with any awkwardly shaped workpiece, and the collet clamp is no exception. Position the blank roughly at first, check the centre of the ⁹/₁₆ in (14.3 mm) hole by eye and make coarse adjustments until you're ready to set it finally with your centring point and DTI. Begin with a centre drill, open up gradually and either ream or bore out the last shreds of metal to reach finished size.

The drill vice is the correct place in which to grip the clamp blank for drilling the tapping hole. Drill right through with a 4 mm drill for 2BA (4.2 mm drill for M5 × 0.8 mm) and open up to half depth with a ¹³/₆₄ in (5.2 mm) drill. When you cut the slit, one half of the hole will be clear and the other half tapping size, which means you have a ready made guide-bush for your 2BA (M5 × 0.8) taps. With the slot cut and the screw hole tapped, all that remains to do is filing, emery cloth work and buffing up.

If you've been dreading the thought of setting up square bar material in the four-jaw chuck to turn the ⁵/₁₆ in (8 mm) diameters on the knuckles, we're going to put you out of your misery. There's a little trick you can use to avoid this, and put the square blanks in the three-jaw SC chuck instead. Measure the distance across the diagonal of your square bar or, if you're good at maths, you'll know that the diagonal of a square is 1.14 times the side. Don't take this result too literally. Better to caliper the diagonal or measure it with a micrometer to get a more reliable figure.

Add ¼ in (6.4 mm) to the diagonal dimension and turn a short length of bar to this diameter. What you're making is a little sleeve just long enough to be gripped for its full length by the jaws of the SC chuck (**Fig. 63**) (our chuck will grip ¾ in (19 mm) of bar). Drill or bore out the bar to fit closely over the corners of the square and part-off the length of sleeve you need. All you have to do now is make a saw-slit along the sleeve and squeeze the square bar inside it with the right amount projecting at the front. Put the whole thing in the three-jaw, with the slit between two of the jaws, tighten the jaws on the sleeve and hey presto! The square bar is centralisd in the chuck as accurately as we need for most purposes, and it is firmly held for machining the ⁵⁄₁₆ in (8 mm) diameter.

Cut the ½ in (12.7 mm) square blanks together and turn all the ⁵⁄₁₆ in (8 mm) diameters at one chuck setting. Leave the marking out and other operations until all the stalk-turning is done and the components fit closely into the base collet. If they come out a trifle small don't worry, unless they are too small to be properly gripped by the collet clamp. In this event, you'll have no choice but to make new ones. The degreasing, blueing and marking out of the knuckles can be done next, with fixed and moving vice jaws clamped together for marking. Follow the drawings **(Fig. 61)** and keep checking back to make sure the holes are in the correct relationship to each other *before* you take the blanks to the drill press. Measure twice – cut once!

Keep the two jaws clamped together to drill the two holes almost through at 4 mm for 2BA (4.2 mm for M5 × 0.8 mm) and cut the gap (which is a slot, in reality) at right angles to them. Do the whole thing with a slot drill in the miller or by drilling,

Fig. 62. A perspective view of the split collet clamp.

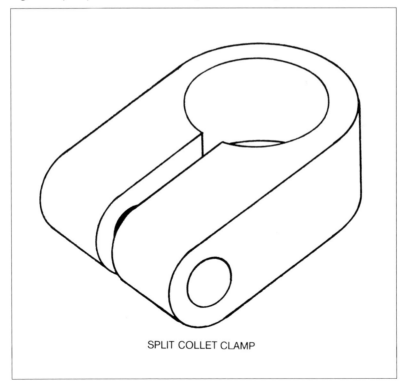

SPLIT COLLET CLAMP

sawing, and filing to the lines (**Fig. 64**). *Do not* try to use a slot drill in your drilling machine – the drill press spindle bearings are not designed for the side loads encountered in milling operations. Take off the clamps, when the slot is finished, and open out the holes in the moving jaw to $^{13}\!/_{64}$ in (5.2 mm). Mill, or saw off, the 30° slope and finish with files and emery cloth.

Drill and ream the $^{5}\!/_{16}$ in (8 mm) holes in the knuckles, tap-drill the clamping holes (4 mm or 4.2 mm) right through and open out halfway with a $^{13}\!/_{64}$ in (5.2 mm) drill before cutting the slits. We have indicated a radius on the end of the knuckle but this is a matter of personal taste. Tap the blind holes in the fixed jaw of the vice, clean, degrease and prepare them to receive the threaded ends of the vice screw and guide rod, which you can cement in as soon as they are ready. The threaded rods are pieces of $^{3}\!/_{16}$ in (4.8 mm) dia bar with a simple bit of thread cut on the ends. Remember the procedure for using anaerobic adhesives and read the maker's leaflet. When the rods are secure, the vice can be assembled, ready to receive its nut. This is not the same as the other screws and it must be made in two operations. First, drill the 2BA (M5 × 0.8 mm) tapping size hole right through and open it out to $^{25}\!/_{64}$ in (10 mm) diameter for a depth of $^{5}\!/_{8}$ in (16 mm), before tapping it. Skim the $^{5}\!/_{8}$ in (16 mm) diameter and knurl a 1 in (25.4 mm) length for the finger grip. Turn the work end for end in the chuck, grip it on the knurled surface with card or shim to protect the finish, and turn the $^{3}\!/_{8}$ in (9.5 mm) diameter and the sloping face.

Slip the spring over the screw, fit the moving jaw, and when the nut is put on to its screw your instrument maker's vice can be assembled by fitting the stalks into the knuckles and into the base collet – as you decide – to place the vice itself where you need it for comfortable work on tiny parts. We designed this vice to be used with the screw and guide rod at the back, out of the

Fig. 63. Our homemade 'collet' gripping square bar for turning in the three-jaw chuck. Note that the split is located between two jaws.

Fig. 64. The gap between the fixed and the moving jaws being drilled out.

way of saws and files when you're working on the 'fixed-jaw' side. So many small vices force you to have all the hardware at the front, making angular sawing and filing in that plane almost impossible.

Bolting the vice to the bench may not be a good plan for some workers, depending on the height, position and size of the chosen bench top. It might be better to fix the vice to a chunk of wood or chipboard heavy enough not to shift around while you're working on something delicate. If you prefer sitting down for delicate work then clamp the block of wood in the bench vice and sit beside it (**Fig. 58**). You'll be surprised how comfortable this can be, and remember, if you spend long hours at your bench you're cutting the risk of lower-back pain.

If you are one of the growing number of metal-workers who like to see their workshop equipment kept in purpose-made wooden cases, the instrument maker's vice will gladden your heart. It strips down into sections which would look great, set into velvet inside a polished wood box with those brass fasteners. But let's stop daydreaming because it's time for us to get on with the mandrel press we started in Chapter 2.

8 MANDREL PRESS

Way back in Chapter 2, you made a pair of columns with reduced diameters at each end and identical shoulder lengths, for the mandrel press we're going to make next (**Fig. 65**). Now is the time to get them out, dust them off and cut a thread on each of those smaller diameters. We don't want a thread right up to the shoulder, just enough to take a full nut, in this case ½ in (12.7 mm). Have a good look at the general arrangement drawing (**Fig. 66**) and the details in **Fig. 67** and you'll see what we mean. If your lathe mandrel will take a ¾ in (19 mm) round bar through its bore, you can skip the next bit because you won't need to cut the thread between centres, you can do it in the three-jaw chuck.

However, we ordinary mortals should now set up the lathe for turning between centres. Let's briefly recap on what we need to do. Off comes the chuck, to be replaced by the catchplate with a dead centre in the socket of the mandrel nose. Another centre, preferably a running centre, goes into the socket of the tailstock

Fig. 65. Pressing the square bar into the split collet with our simple mandrel press.

Fig. 66. General
arrangement of the
simple mandrel
press.

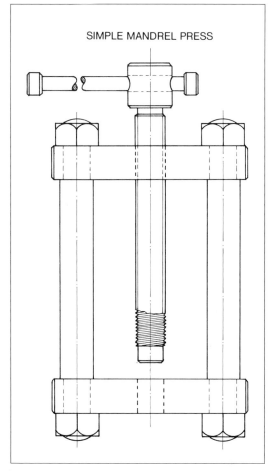

Fig. 66. General arrangement of the simple mandrel press.

SIMPLE MANDREL PRESS

barrel. When you've done all this, and sorted out a lathe carrier of a suitable size to fasten on the ⅝ in (16 mm) diameter of the workpiece, you're ready to start.

Put a spot of lubricant in each of the centre holes of the first workpiece and set it up between centres. Look at the tool chart (**Fig. 124**) and identify the external screwcutting tool. You will need one that is small in width rather than the type with a full width shape (**Fig. 68**). The one we will be using is ground down to about ³⁄₁₆ in (4.8 mm) wide at the shank, with an included angle of 55°.

We will be cutting a BSF thread, which has an angle of 55°, but other types of thread might call for different tool point angles – for instance, the metric thread form requires a 60° angle. To ensure that we're all speaking the same language, the parts of a screw thread are identified in **Fig. 69**.

To make things easier, we want you to start by cutting a relief groove where the thread finishes. You can do this with a recessing tool or a parting tool of ⅛ in (3.2 mm) tip width or

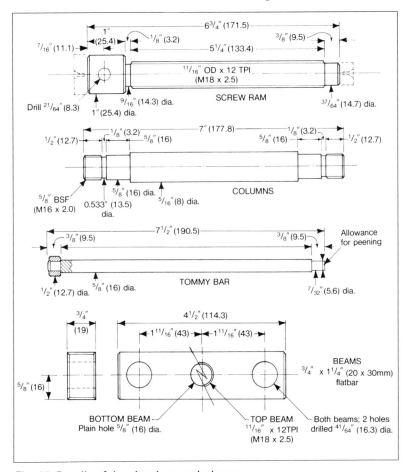

Fig. 67. Details of the simple mandrel press.

Fig. 68. The usefulness of a reduced-width external screwcutting tool.

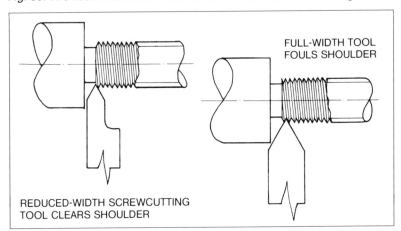

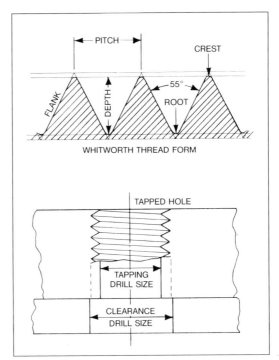

Fig. 69. Things you should know about screw threads.

PITCH

CREST

55°

FLANK

DEPTH

ROOT

WHITWORTH THREAD FORM

TAPPED HOLE

TAPPING
DRILL SIZE

CLEARANCE
DRILL SIZE

less, but don't cut the groove until you know how deep to go. The way to find this out is to look it up in thread data tables in the column marked *'Thread Depth'*. In our tables the depth of thread for ⅝ in BSD (M16 × 2.0) is given as 0.0457 in (1.16 mm) or 1.23 mm for M16. If you feed in the tool to this depth and no deeper, later when the point of the screwcutting tool reaches the correct depth it will scratch the bottom surface of the relief groove. Apart from this advantage, the relief groove gives you somewhere for the tool point to go when it has finished its cutting traverse and you want to stop the lathe.

There's a lot of unnecessary panic about screwcutting, even among people who take all other aspects of lathework in their stride. We think it's like any other new skill – at first it will seem tricky but later you'll wonder why you worried. Clamp your screwcutting tool in the toolpost, taking particular care to set it on centre height. Taper turning and screwcutting are two processes for which the tool point must be on centre height, otherwise the results you get won't be what you wanted. The screwcutting tool is special in another way, too. The tool point angle must be presented to the work so that its centre line is at right angles to the lathe axis. **Fig. 70** shows a handy gauge being used to achieve this aim. If you don't check these little details you may finish up with a thread which has a 20° angle on one flank and a 35° angle on the other.

So – you've got your workpiece between centres and your screwcutting tool set up in the toolpost; what next? You can –

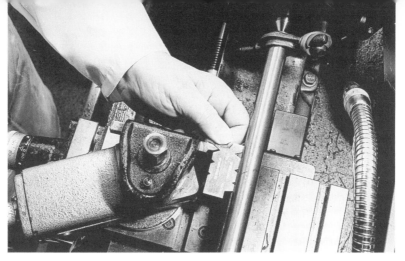

and many do — carry on and cut the thread as things stand, so that the tool cuts on both flanks at each pass and each application of cut. But it isn't the ideal way and the finish on the thread is not as good as by the method we prefer. A better way, we think, is to set the tool to cut on the left hand flank only. This means there is only about half the cutting load on the tool for the same amount of cut and we get this result by swinging over the topslide (**Fig. 71**). The thread angle is 55° for BSF (60° for metric threads), so we set over the topslide to half that amount, 27½° (or 30°), swinging the feed handle towards the tailstock. You will, of course, have to reposition the tool point to the setting gauge. When you've done all this, zero the topslide thimble, and then all that remains is to set the lathe speed and arrange the right ratio of auto feed to cut the thread.

We know people who would run the lathe at 200 rpm to cut a thread of this diameter and if you are experienced you can get away with it. But we're speaking to people who are not that experienced, when we say stick to fastest backgear speed for a start (80 or 100 rpm) and take everything nice and steadily.

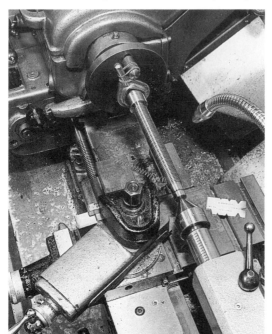

Above *Fig. 70. Use of a tool point gauge to set the screwcutting tool to its correct angle.*

Left *Fig. 71. The thread being cut on the press ram with topslide set over to 27½°.*

Right *Fig. 72. The difference between perpendicular movement and actual tool travel with the topslide set over.*

Making the tool travel the required distance along the work-piece for each revolution of the mandrel is managed differently on different lathes. Some have changewheels, some have belts or geared heads and some have a quick change gearbox. However you do this on your lathe, do it now! We'll be running a check to see that the pitch is what it should be, before we begin serious thread cutting. Your lathe handbook, or the people you bought the lathe from, will tell you what your particular ratio-setting procedure should be. Many lathes also have tables attached to the machine, which show gear combinations for all kinds of threads.

Next, do the usual check. With the mandrel stopped, traverse the saddle along the length of the proposed cut to find out whether the toolpost fouls any part of the set up. If it's all clear, then start the lathe, kiss the surface of the work with the tool point and zero the thimble on your topslide and cross-slide feed handles. Rack the tool along to the relief groove, feed the tip inwards until it 'kisses' the surface at the bottom of the groove and note down the reading. (Since the topslide is swung over, this will not be the 'thread depth' figure. The tool point will move further than it would if the travel was at right angles to the work (**Fig. 72**). You will need the cross-slide movement to back the tool out of its cut at the end of a run, and with it zeroed, you can return the tool point to exactly the right place each pass.

With the tool point kissing the work, rack it to the right with the carriage handwheel until you have a $\frac{1}{16}$ in (1.6 mm) or so of space between the tool and the start of the thread. Start the lathe and engage the half-nuts (auto-feed lever). The tool will advance to the left and scratch a helical line on the $\frac{5}{8}$ in (16 mm) diameter, whereupon you smartly stop the lathe, *without disengaging the half-nuts*, just as the tool point enters the relief groove. Now put a rule on the scatched lines and measure the

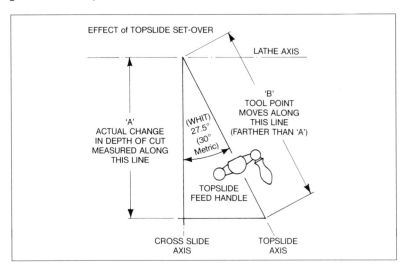

pitch. It it comes out at 14 TPI for BSF (or 2 mm for M16) you are clear to proceed. If it doesn't, there could be several reasons why that is so. You could have misread the tables and set up a faulty gear train, or your quick-change gearbox levers could have been wrongly set. Check around, re-set the ratio, and persevere until you get the correct pitch.

We've talked longer than usual at the beginning of a project, but this groundwork is vitally important in screwcutting. Wind out the cross-slide to pull the tool away from the work. Start the lathe with the mandrel running in reverse so that the carriage travels from left to right and the tool ends up at the start of the thread. *Keep the half nuts engaged.* When the tool point is clear of the start, stop the lathe and wind in the cross-slide to the zero mark. Put on a 2 thou (0.05 mm) cut with the topslide handle, apply cutting fluid or coolant as desired, and make your first pass along the workpiece until the tool reaches the relief groove. With the half-nuts still engaged, wind out the cross-slide and repeat the whole sequence. Go on repeating the whole process, keeping a close eye on the finish being produced, until the tool point scratches a line on the bottom of the relief groove. This means the thread has reached full depth and can be tested with a suitable nut. As cut, the thread will have a sharp crest and this should be removed with a file or chaser to give you the kind of close fit in the nut that gives your heart a lift. If the nut is too tight, take another very fine cut, and so on. Of course, if you happen to have access to the correct size die, all you need do is to cut the thread to within a whisker of finished size and then run the die over it to finish it off perfectly.

More experienced workers will tell you about the thread dial. This is a device geared to the leadscrew in such a way that it indicates to the turner when his workpiece is in exactly the right position for the half-nuts to be re-engaged so that the advancing tool point hits the correct groove and continues to cut the thread as though the nuts had not been opened. If you think you can handle this, in addition to all the other considerations, read it up and have a go. But for the moment we recommend taking it more cautiously.

The ends of the two columns are exactly the same, and by the time you have screwcut the last one, you'll be a veteran. Put them safely aside for a while and cut yourself a piece of 1 in (25.4 mm) dia BMS, 7½ in (190.5 mm) long for the screw ram. Although the drawing **(Fig. 67)** calls for a piece 6¾ in (171.7 mm) long, we're trying to make the job as beautiful as possible. We're going to turn and screwcut the ram between centres, which means there'll be an unsightly centre hole in each end. The top hole is only of cosmetic interest, agreed, but the bottom one — the nose of the ram — needs to be flat. You don't want the ends of small shafts disappearing into the centre hole while you're trying to press them, do you? We thought it would make a far better job if we left extra metal at the ends and removed it later, to leave those smooth faces we all know and love.

Prepare the ends of the workpiece by centre-drilling, using the 'fixed steady' method described in Chapter 2, and set it up between centres. We're afraid you'll have to take out the screwcutting tool for the moment. Put either a T&F tool or a knife tool into the toolpost, whichever you prefer for shaft turning, and set it to centre height. Our first job is to reduce the diameter from 1 in (25.4 mm) to ¹¹⁄₁₆ in (17.5 mm) for a distance of 6⅛ in (155.6 mm) from the right-hand end. Set the lathe speed at around 400 rpm, the horizontal feed at about 5 thou (0.13 mm) per rev, and apply a cut of 15 thou (0.38 mm). Neither the exact length of the reduced diameter nor the finish on the newly turned surface is of critical importance, because the whole of the reduced diameter is going to be screwcut 12 TPI, Whitworth form.

You may have noticed something strange about the sizes of the relief groove and the straight 'nose' portion shown in **Fig. 67**. We're using a slightly different procedure this time, to give you an alternative method for use when needed on other projects ('there's more ways of skinning a cat' etc). In screwcutting the columns, we cut the relief groove to the thread core diameter. On the ram drawing you will note that the relief groove is deeper – ⁹⁄₁₆ in (14.3 mm) diameter (13.5 mm for M18), making the groove ¹⁄₁₆ in (1.6 mm) deep – and there is another reduced diameter of ³⁷⁄₆₄ in (14.7 mm) at the nose end. When you have set up your screwcutting gear ratio, to cut the correct pitch thread, and zeroed the cross-slide on the ¹¹⁄₁₆ in (17.5 mm) diameter, check the thread depth for 12 TPI in your tables and you'll see that the tool point will cut its scratch line at 0.053 in (1.36 mm) depth along the nose diameter. On the other hand, when the tool has cut the thread to its full depth its point will still be well clear of the relief groove diameter. In this way you get an early warning when the tool is almost at full thread depth instead of having to wait until it reaches the relief groove. Remember, on this job the tool travels 5¼ in (133.4 mm) from one end of the thread to the other! Using the same procedure as you did for the columns, go ahead and cut the long thread. When it's finished, we'll be able to use it to gauge the internal thread in the top beam.

Change the screwcutting tool for a parting tool and cut a ⅛ in (3.2 m) groove at each end of the workpiece to mark off its finished length. Measure 1 in (25.4 mm) from the left side of the relief groove for the left hand parting groove, and ⅜ in (9.5 mm) to the right, from the start of the thread for the right hand groove. Cut good size chamfers on the corners of the 1 in (25.4 mm) diameter portion and a slightly smaller chamfer on the nose of the ram. That's the turning and screwcutting finished, now all that remains to do on the ram is to take off the extra bits at the ends and cross-drill it for the tommy bar. This procedure should be quite familiar, by now. Blue the head face of the ram and set up the threaded portion in vee blocks; treat it gently, find the centre line and scribe it right across the face and along both sides. Measure $\frac{7}{16}$ in (11.1 mm) from the end and centre pop for the $\frac{21}{64}$ in (8.3 mm) dia cross-drilled hole. Using the scribed line and an engineers' square, set up the ram in the drilling vice with card or shim to protect the threads. Pick up the pop mark with your centring point and drill the hole, starting with a $\frac{1}{8}$ in (3.2 mm) or $\frac{3}{16}$ in (4.8 mm) drill and finish out with a $\frac{21}{64}$ in (8.3 mm) drill. It would be a nice touch to countersink both ends of this hole, to allow for bruising of the edges during a busy working life.

The top beam (**Fig. 67**) has a threaded hole at its centre, into which the ram is screwed. The other two holes are to clear the threaded ends of the columns. You'll have to cut the thread with an internal screwcutting tool (**Fig. 124**) using the ram's thread as your gauge. Now you can see the added advantage of having a core-size diameter at the nose end of the ram. You can use this to gauge when your bored hole has reached core size for the $\frac{11}{16}$ in (17.5 mm) internal thread.

First things first! Cut two pieces of $\frac{3}{4}$ in (19 mm) $\times$ 1¼ in (31.8 mm) flat BMS bar, each 4½ in (114.3 mm) long, and file or mill them square at the ends. Blue one wide face of each bar and mark out the positions of the holes, making firm centre pop marks at all the centre positions. Drill the outer holes and use them to fix the beam on to a face plate on ¼ in (6.4 mm) packing and centre it with the centring point or a wiggler (**Fig. 73**). What's a wiggler? That's another kind of centring device which is held in the toolpost or the tailstock chuck, so called because when the point is engaged with an eccentric pop mark – it wiggles! The idea is to adjust the position of the workpiece until the wiggler stops wiggling!

When the pop mark is running true, drill out in stages until you have come as close as you can to core diameter, which is

Fig. 73. A wiggler being used to centre the 'tapping' hole in the top beam.

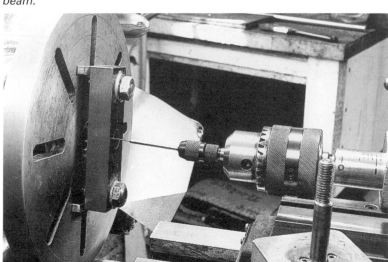

Fig. 74. Screwcutting the central hole in the top beam. Note that the topslide ball handle is replaced with a plain bush, and the coolant standpipe has been removed.

0.580 in for the $^9/_{16}$ in thread or 14.5 mm for an 18 mm thread. Put a sharp small boring tool into the toolpost and set it on, or just above, centre height. Take fine cuts out of the bore (with a scrap of masking tape stuck to the tool shank to show you when you're nearly at the other end of the hole). Using the small end of the ram as a gauge, stop boring when the nose slips smoothly into the bore with no rattle. You have reached thread core diameter, and it's time to seek out your internal screwcutting tool. Take out the boring tool, and set up the screwcutting tool exactly on centre height.

For the most part, the process of internal screwcutting is identical with that for cutting threads on the outside of shafts (**Fig. 74**) but, of course, there are some differences. Swinging over the topslide, to cut down the flank of a thread, may be difficult on some lathes and impossible on others. The topslide handle on our lathe got in the way, so we took it off and replaced it with a bush (**Fig. 74**).

Otherwise, proceed as before, keeping the half-nuts engaged and reversing the mandrel to send the saddle back to the beginning. There's one more *vital* thing to remember: as you're cutting on the inside surface, the point of the tool is facing towards you. This means that to put on cut, you have to turn the cross-slide handle *anticlockwise* not clockwise as you normally do. Also, you must turn the cross-slide handle clockwise to make the tool point clear the thread for the return journey. Take little cuts all the way, and when you are approaching finishing size take two runs through the threaded hole each time *without* increasing the cut in either direction. The 'spring' in the tool shank will cause the cutting edge to remove a little more material on the second pass. Only gauge the thread with the threaded ram, after the second pass had been made at any one setting.

We are aiming for a smooth, but not loose, sliding fit of the ram in the top beam. When you've achieved this, take the top beam off the face plate and put on the bottom beam, packed and

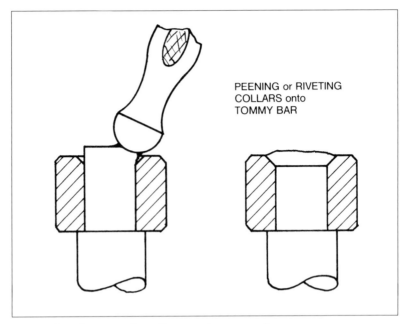

PEENING or RIVETING
COLLARS onto
TOMMY BAR

Fig. 75. Peening over the collars on the tommy bar.

clamped, in the same way. After you have cut this internal thread, boring out a smooth sided 15 mm (0.591 in) diameter hole ought to seem like child's play. The central hole diameter is not important, but a smooth finish on the surface of the bore will look good. If you wish, you can ream the hole after drilling. It would also be good practice, we think, to slightly countersink the hole with the boring tool. The countersunk end should face upwards when the press is assembled.

Take off external sharp corners with a smooth file and if you've located suitable ⅝ in (16 mm) or M16 nuts, the frame of your mandrel press is ready to go together. You might put locking washers of some kind under the nuts to prevent them coming loose in the heat of battle. Be sure, before you do, that you're not going to need to take the frame apart again. Those locking washers make a nasty mess if you have to remove the nuts.

The only parts left to make, now, are the tommy bar and its collars. The bar itself (**Fig. 67**) is a plain length of ⁵⁄₁₆ in (8 mm) dia BMS reduced to ⁷⁄₃₂ in (5.6 mm) dia for a short distance each end, leaving a shoulder length of 6¾ in (171.5 mm). When the reduced ends are finished, the main diameter should be given a bright shine with emery cloth. The collars (**Fig. 67**) are like thick washers, except that one end of the central hole is deeply countersunk and both outside corners are given a healthy chamfer.

To attach one of the collars, grip the bar firmly in the vice with the shoulder of one reduced end just projecting above the jaws. You'll be gripping on a cleaned-up surface, so use soft jaws or strips of heavy card. Slip the collar over the smaller diameter with its countersink upwards, and spread the bar into the countersink with moderate hammer blows, preferably with the ball pein end of the hammer (**Fig. 75**). A few heavy blows would, of course, secure the collar. But more blows, spread evenly with an eye to the shape you are producing, will give a pleasing finish. Don't get carried away by your success and forget that you can only fit *one* collar at this stage. The second one goes on *after* you've inserted the tommy bar into the head of the ram. More care is needed when riveting the second collar, to avoid damaging the ram with either the vice or the hammer.

Run the ram into its threaded hole in the top beam and your mandrel press is ready to use. You can use it vertically, with the bottom beam gripped in the vice (remembering the soft jaws) or horizontally with one column in the vice jaws. You'll be impressed by the number of jobs you find for this little device to do. Anything from pressing the spindles out of watch gears, to force-fitting oil retaining bearing bushes – our mandrel press will make light work of it.

9 LIGHT DUTY WINCH

Until now, we've been concerned with lathe work — putting things in the chuck and between centres to work on them. We have done the odd bit of drilling and tapping, and a little sawing and filing to finish things off. That was intended to get you used to the idea that all of an engineer's work isn't done in the lathe. The next project, a light duty winch (**Fig. 76**) is a very basic machine and several parts of it will require more benchwork than turning. Whatever line of work you decide to specialise in, benchwork is gong to form a large part of it.

We're going to begin with the side plates for the winch, which are made together out of pieces of ¼ in (6.4 mm) hot rolled steel plate (**Fig. 77**). When we say we make the side plates together, we mean that literally. When we have some holes drilled in each of the plates they can be screwed together for the rest of the operations. But our first task is to transfer the dimensions from the drawings (**Figs. 78 & 79**) on to the material, and to do this we need two straight edges at right angles to each other on each

Left *Fig. 76. The light duty winch before being given its rope. The rope-securing screw can be seen on the hardwood drum.*

Above right *Fig. 77. An exploded view of the light duty winch.*

Right *Fig. 78. Details of the light duty winch.*

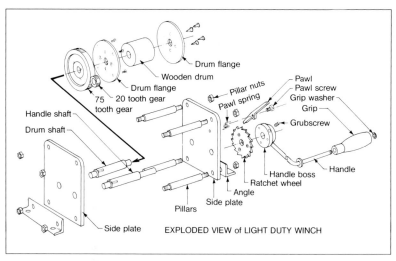

EXPLODED VIEW of LIGHT DUTY WINCH

- Drum flange
- Wooden drum
- Drum flange
- 75 tooth gear
- 20 tooth gear
- Handle shaft
- Drum shaft
- Pillar nuts
- Pawl spring
- Pawl
- Pawl screw
- Grip washer
- Grip
- Grubscrew
- Handle boss
- Handle
- Ratchet wheel
- Angle
- Side plate
- Pillars
- Side plate

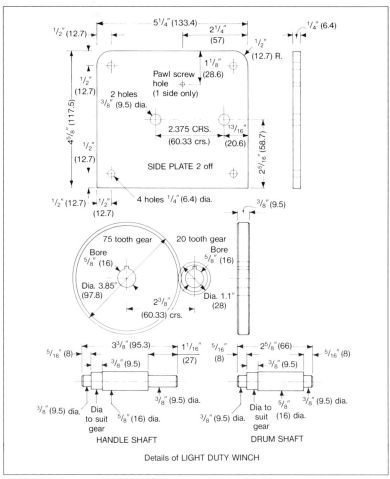

Details of LIGHT DUTY WINCH

SIDE PLATE 2 off

75 tooth gear
20 tooth gear

HANDLE SHAFT

DRUM SHAFT

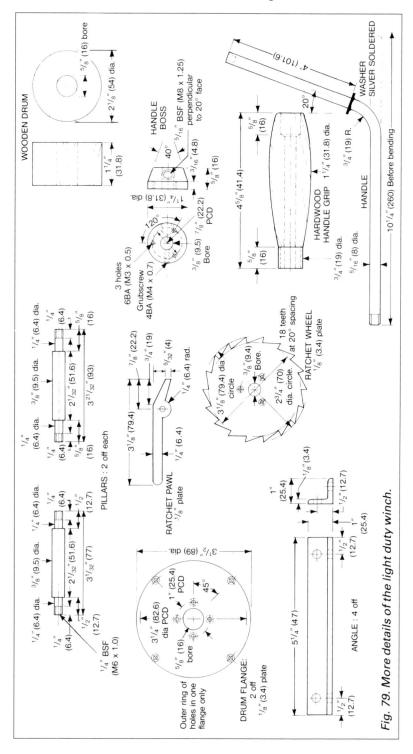

Fig. 79. More details of the light duty winch.

piece (datum edges). A word of warning: if you get your plates from a fabrication firm they will almost certainly cut them for you on a heavy duty guillotine, unless you can persuade them to profile-cut them with oxy-acetylene equipment. Guillotining can distort the edges of your plate until it won't lie flat on a reference surface and you have to 'correct' it with a heavy hammer. Profiling leaves an uneven edge, but the cut plate will be quite flat. Ask for a little extra metal outside the marked line for cleaning up.

If you're lucky enough to own, or have access to, a vertical milling machine, you'll have no problems cleaning up the edges of the plates to finished size. If not, a few minutes spent filing to a square and a straight-edge will get you to the same place – and think how much good the exercise will do for your arm muscles. When you have your two datum edges, lay one plate aside and concentrate on the other one, first coating one face with opaque white marking fluid. With Jenny Oddlegs (**Fig. 40**) and rule, mark out for the four corner holes. The drawing (**Fig. 78**) calls for these holes to finish at ¼ in (6.4 mm) diameter, to take the ends of the pillars which will eventually hold them together. But we'll start out with a smaller size hole because we're going to dowel the two plates together before we bore out the shaft hole.

Mark out the centres of the shaft holes next, not worrying too much about the 2⅜ in (60.33 mm) dimension at this stage, but getting as near as you can to it with rule, square and scriber. Lightly centre pop the six hole positions and clamp the two plates together with their datum edges aligned as closely as you can get them. A little extra care with this pays dividends when you come to assemble your machine. Toolmaker's clamps are ideal for this purpose, but C-clamps or powerful spring clamps will do if you're careful. Clamp the assembly to the drill press table with packings to clear the clamps, and when the plates are tightly held parallel with the table surface, drill two diagonally opposite corner holes with a ⅛ in (3.2 mm) drill, followed by a ¼ in (6.4 mm) drill. Don't rush the job, or the plates might shift and all your careful marking out will go for nothing.

Deburr the holes on the back of the lower plate and put ¼ in (6.4 mm) screws, with nuts and washers, through the holes with the screw heads underneath. Tighten the nuts down firmly. Take out the ¼ in (6.4 mm) drill, put in a ⅛ in (3.2 mm) drill, to start the remaining two holes and finish out to ¹⁵⁄₆₄ in (6 mm). Put the drill on a low speed for reaming and use plenty of neat cutting oil, clearing the swarf frequently with a stiff brush. Pass a ¼ in (6.4 mm) reamer almost, but not quite, through the plates at each of the smaller holes. Reamers have a 'lead' at the business end, which means if you don't take them right through the job a small amount of metal will be left in the diameter at the lower end of the holes. We need this extra metal now.

The idea of dowelling two components together – much used

Fig. 80. Winch sideplates clamped down on the drill press table for drilling and reaming for dowels. One dowel can be seen, left of the reamer.

in the machine tool industry – is for the parts to be accurately located and yet easily separated when necessary. In the present case, the dowels are only temporary and the holes will be needed for bolting later, but the same rule applies. The dowel is held fast in the lower plate while the top plate could be easily removed. Cut two ½ in (12.7 mm) lengths of ¼ in (6.4 mm) silver steel for the dowels (not that we need the special properties of the material, just its accurate sizing on the diameter) and chamfer the ends. Using the bench vice or a mandrel press, force the dowel to the bottom of the hole – all the way through both plates. Do not use a hammer to drive the dowel in, there is too great a risk that it will not be precisely positioned and will be distorted by the blow. Even if the dowel itself survived, the plate material might be distorted around the rim of the hole, rendering the dowel useless. Don't rush it! Use a vice, where you can see exactly what's happening and be in control all the time (**Fig. 80**).

The plates are fastened tightly together and their relative position is fixed by dowels. Now you can seek out those toolmakers buttons you made in Chapter 1. You'll need two – a long one and a short one – and two screws to fasten them to the workpiece. When you've found the buttons, suitable screws and washers (**Fig. 2**), you can drill tapping size holes on the centre pop marks for the shaft holes. The hole through the button is ⁵⁄₁₆ in (8 mm) dia, but we need some room for sideways adjustment so we wouldn't use screws bigger than about ¼ in (6.4 mm) diameter. Let's say ¼ in BSF (M6 × 1.0) for which we need a tapping hole 5.3 mm dia for ¼ in BSF (5 mm dia for M6). Drill the tapping holes and start the threads in the drill press, removing the job to the bench to complete the tapping.

Loosely screw the longer of the two buttons to the tapped hole nearer the edge of the plate, setting it ⁹⁄₁₆ in (14.3 mm) from the edge with a rule. When you're satisfied with its positioning, tighten it down and screw the shorter button loosely to the other tapped hole. When we say 'loosely' in this case we don't mean that the button should be moveable with the fingers. It should be held firmly enough not to be easily knocked out of place, but not so firmly that some force must be used to adjust its position. The distance between the centres of the two gears is very important, if they are to mesh properly when the winch is assembled. To measure the centre distance accurately, we must use a 2–3 in (50–75 mm) micrometer or a 6 in (150 mm) vernier caliper. Because we're using buttons of accurately turned outside diameter we can calculate the required dimension and measure over the two buttons (**Fig. 81**). All we need to know is the figure we must add to the actual centre distance. The drawing shows 2⅜ in (60.33 mm) between centres. The buttons are ½ in (12.7 mm) diameter, which means we must add ¼ in (6.4 mm) (half the diameter of one button) at each end of the centre distance like this: 2⅜ in (60.33 mm) + 2¼ in (6.4 mm) = 2⅞ in (2.875 in) (73 mm). If your buttons are both the same standard diameter you need only add the diameter of one button to the centre distance and you have your required caliper measurement. While you're adjusting the button and checking the measurement with the caliper, check also the distance from the bottom edge of the plate, which should be the same for both buttons. Adjust the second button by tapping with a brass hammer and a drift or a piece of hardwood, but nothing which might bruise the turned surface. When the caliper reads exactly 2.875 in (73 mm), finally tighten down the screw. The assembly is now ready to go into the lathe – but how?

Fig. 81. Taking measurements over two toolmaker's buttons with a 2–3 in (5–75 mm) micrometer.

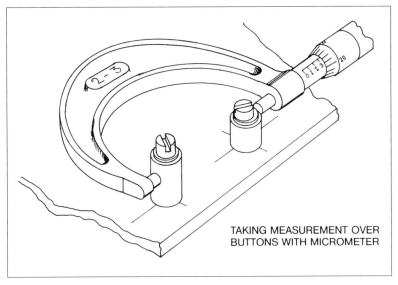

TAKING MEASUREMENT OVER
BUTTONS WITH MICROMETER

Fig. 82. The second (shorter) button being centred on the lathe faceplate with a soft drift and DTI.

It will not go into either of the chucks, and if it did, the jaws wouldn't close enough for you to be able to swing it. The answer is to use the face plate (**Fig. 82**) with three or four clamps and some parallel packing pieces. The clamps bolt down through the slots in the faceplate and the packings hold the work level with the surface and give clearance for the boring tools to pass through without hitting the mandrel nose. We would advise using ⅜ in (9.5 mm) packing at this stage in your career. It will give you more space to see what's happening and more time to stop the traverse when you reach the end of the boring cut. When you get really adept and all the control movements are second nature to you, you can reduce this 'safety insurance', depending – of course – on the nature of the work.

We found that when we'd bolted the job to the faceplate and offered it up to the mandrel nose, we had a problem. One of the sharp corners of the plate assembly was catching on the lathe bed. Some nifty work with a coarse file soon remedied this, and off we went.

With the plates clamped to the faceplate and the taller button running true by eye, set up your DTI so that the tip of the plunger registers movement on the surface of the button through one complete revolution of the workpiece. This is a good time to check that the plunger clears the top of the second button as the work revolves. You'll see, from **Fig. 82**, that we cheated a bit by using a different type of DTI. Using a soft hammer, or an ordinary hammer and drift, tap the work in the required directions to get the button running absolutely true (**Fig. 82**). Remember to lift the plunger tip off the button before you hit the workpiece with the hammer. If you don't do this, the shock of the hammer blow will be transmitted up the plunger to the delicate mechanism inside the 'clock'. Delicate instruments respond to careful treatment by giving long and trouble-free service.

Remove the DTI, unscrew and take off the button you have just set true, and prepare to bore out the first shaft hole. Let us digress for a moment, because the words 'shaft hole' are worrying us. We are trying to behave like engineers, and that means using the correct terms so that others know exactly what we mean. 'Shaft holes' doesn't carry exactly the right picture; a hole is what you put a bolt through. Shafts carrying pulleys or gears run in bearings, so let's call the hole we're going to bore the shaft bearing. If it doesn't do anything for you at the moment, it makes us feel you're picking up good habits rather than not-so-good ones.

Check that everything is firmly tightened down and you're ready to begin. Start by drilling out the threads in the tapped hole with a ⁵⁄₁₆ in (8 mm) drill. Now there are two ways of finishing the shaft bearing bore. You can follow with an ¹¹⁄₃₂ in (8.7 mm) drill and a small boring tool, boring to exactly ³⁄₈ in (9.5 mm) and the finish will be quite acceptable as a bearing surface for this application. If you want to make the finish on your shaft bearing even better you could ream out the bearing bores after a skim with the boring tool, and turn the shaft ends to a close running fit. The essence of good reaming practice is to leave only a whisker of material to be removed from the hole. Watch for the tool coming through both plates and check that the toolpost doesn't catch the faceplate clamps.

That's the first hole bored. Now you can slacken the clamps and move the plates until the remaining button is in roughly the right place. Retighten the clamps enough to begin centring the button, by eye, as before. When the button is centred accurately with the DTI, you can finally tighten the clamps. After removing the DTI, unscrewing and taking off the button and winding the boring tool out of your way, you can put the ⁵⁄₁₆ in (8 mm) drill back in the tailstock chuck and begin drilling out. Follow the same procedure as we did for the first shaft bearing and you will

Fig. 83. Drawfiling the edges of the sideplates.

end up with two accurate ⅜ in (9.5 mm) bores with their centres exactly 2⅜ in or 2.375 in (60.33 mm) apart, just as the drawing specified.

To complete the sideplates, take them off the faceplate, remove the screws and nuts, prise the top plate off the dowels and remove the dowels with pliers or a self-grip wrench. If the dowels prove stubborn, turn the lower plate on its back, with packings under it, and tap them out with a pin punch. Open out all four of the corner holes with a ¹⁷⁄₆₄ in (6.7 mm) dia drill, and mill (or saw and file) a ½ in (12.7 mm) radius on the top two corners. Finish off the edges by drawfiling (**Fig. 83**) and take off any remaining sharp corners before putting the sideplates away, for the moment.

By the time you read this you will have had some experience of most of the processes you can carry out on a lathe (except for milling – which is beyond the scope of this book – and indexing, coming in Chapter 11). We think it is time you had a go on your own. We'll give you tips on some points of difficulty, so that you can get on with the job instead of spending too much time reading. If you're not sure which bit is which on the detail drawings (**Figs. 78** & **79**) try the 'exploded' view (**Fig. 77**). The various drawings together should tell you all you need to know to complete the light duty winch.

The gears we used are spares from a set of lathe change wheels. They are described in the literature as 20DP (Diametral Pitch). One has 20 teeth and the other 75 teeth. All the dimensions are given in **Figs. 78** & **79**. You may choose gears of differing sizes or of a different thickness. It is a simple matter to adjust sizes of the other components to suit, and it would be good experience. Whichever pair of gears you use make sure the ratio is roughly the same (3.75:1) and that each gear has a keyway cut in the bore. If you want to check the ratio, mesh the gears, chalk mark one tooth on each, and see how many revs the small gear makes for one complete revolution of the big gear. Or, if you want the easy way, count the teeth and divide the number of teeth on the small gear into the number on the big gear.

If you make the drum flanges early on, you can use the left hand drum flange as a template to drill tapping holes into the inner face of the large gear.

The shape of the pillars will look familiar. They're exactly the same as the pillars for the mandrel press, except that the dimensions are smaller. They do the same job, holding the other parts, in this case the sideplates, the right distance apart and at right angles to the pillars. That's why this type of component is sometimes called a distance piece.

They can be made from ⅜ in (9.5 mm) dia bar, as the larger diameter is not important. The only parts turned are the ends. But the shoulder dimension is important and all four pillars should have the same shoulder length, 2¹⁄₃₂ in (51.6 mm). The threads can be cut with your travelling dieholder, and the outer ends – which will show above the nuts – can be neatened with a knife tool and a smooth file. Note that we've left extra length on the lower pillar threads to allow for the thickness of the angles.

Although the shafts look very much like the pillars, there are important differences. The smaller diameter extensions at the ends are of different lengths and the larger turned diameters must be turned to a push fit in the bore of the gear. It isn't necessary to reduce the diameter of the whole length, just the thickness of the gear and a little to spare. If you have a milling machine, you can cut a keyway in the shaft and file a key to fit it on assembly. If not, drill and tap for two or three ³⁄₁₆ in (4.8 mm) setscrews, which are screwed in tightly and cut off to suit the keyway (**Fig. 84**). They can then be filed to fit the gear keyway on assembly.

The drum assembly consists of two flanges, made from 1.8 in (3.2 mm) sheet steel and a drum made from the hardest wood you have available. We used a piece of afrormosia which has been lying around the workshop for longer than we care to remember. There are one or two pieces of equipment you'll need for these jobs. First, make a stub mandrel (**Fig. 85**) with the

Fig. 84. The use of sawn-off screws, instead of keyway and feather key, to hold shafts.

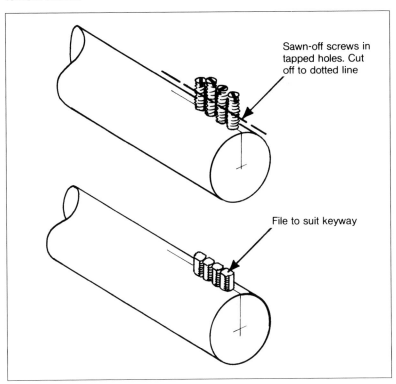

Sawn-off screws in tapped holes. Cut off to dotted line

File to suit keyway

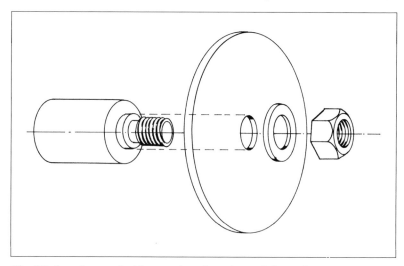

Fig. 85. A stub mandrel for turning the edges of drum flanges.

correct diameter to take the holes in the middle of the flange blanks. For the wooden drum you'll be able to use the gear shaft as a mandrel.

Bore a $^{39}/_{64}$ in (15.5 mm) hole down the centre of the drum blank, press the gear shaft into the hole and turn it parallel in the three-jaw or between centres to 2⅛ in (51.4 mm) dia with a round nose or a T & F tool. Metal turning tools don't do a very good job on wood, but a super finish isn't important in this instance. If you want a better finish, make yourself a wood-turning tool from silver steel. Run a knife tool down the ends to get the 1¼ in (31.8 mm) length right. Remember to cover the lathe bed to keep the wood turnings under control.

Mark out the flanges and the ratchet wheel (see later) on a piece of 1.8 in (3.2 mm) sheet steel and cut them out roughly to shape with a bandsaw or hacksaw. If you've made contact with a firm that does profile cutting that would be even better. Drill the centre holes in all three discs, remembering that the hole in the ratchet wheel is smaller. Ignore the teeth on the ratchet wheel for a moment, put it aside and make the flanges first. Grip the stub mandrel in the three-jaw chuck. Clamp both flanges together, on the stub mandrel and skim the edges to size with a T & F tool. Chamfer the outer corners and remove them from the mandrel. Drill and countersink the eight holes in the left hand flange and the four holes in the right hand flange, remembering to countersink the outer ring of holes on the opposite side to the countersinking of the woodscrew holes. The outer ring of screws goes into the gear and the inner ring into the wooden drum. Deburr the outer edge which was left sharp, slip the drum and the flanges onto the gear shaft and spot the woodscrew holes into the ends of the wooden drum. Drill pilot holes for the woodscrews and drive them home with a little grease or soap on the thread. It is tempting to put in huge woodscrews just to make sure the drum's not going to move, but we wouldn't go larger than 1 in × No. 8.

You could now assemble the larger gear to the drum with countersunk screws of suitable length. The drawing allows for ¹⁄₆₄ in (0.40 mm) clearance at each end of the shafts when they are assembled, so their shoulder length should be checked with that of the pillars.

Another stub mandrel will be needed to skim up the outer diameter of the ratchet wheel blank. While you have it set up in the lathe, scribe a circle ³⁄₁₆ in (4.8 mm) in from the edge. This indicates the depth of the teeth, of which there are 18 at 20° spacing. Mark them out with protractor, dividers and scriber and cut them with hacksaw and file. Careful work will give a pleasing result just as, if the teeth are uneven, it will not go unnoticed! Drill the three fixing holes and countersink them on the side plate face – the teeth at the top should point towards you as you turn the handle **(Fig. 77)**. You can use the ratchet wheel as a template for drilling the three tapped holes in the handle boss. We would leave the making of the ratchet pawl for the time being, until you can check its position on the assembled machine.

The handle boss isn't as simple as it looks on the drawings. It's not the turning – it can be turned on the end of a piece of 1¼ in (31.8 mm) dia bar and parted off when the ³⁄₈ in (9.5 mm) hole through the middle has been reamed to size. Simple! The sloping side is a straightforward piece of taper turning down with the topslide. The three tapped holes in the back are no problem. It's the tapped hole for the handle that might cause a flutter of excitement. This hole is drilled at right angles to the sloping side and, unless you possess a drill vice which you can

Fig. 86. The milling vice being used for drilling the angled hole in the handled boss. The vice is supported on a wooden block with wedges preventing it from moving in relation to its holding down bolts.

tilt up at an angle, you're going to have to work out a way of safely packing up your drill vice to the correct 20° angle. **Fig. 86** shows how we did it, but you'll probably be able to figure out a method of your own. Start drilling with a ⅛ in (3.2 mm) drill, after you've positioned the centre pop mark with your centring point. Open up to the tapping size shown on the drawing, start the thread in the drill press and finish it off in the vice. Take out the packings and lower the base of the vice back on to the drill table to drill and tap the grubscrew hole.

The handle is made from ⁵⁄₁₆ in (8 mm) dia bar, threaded at one end to suit the tapped hole in the boss, with a free-rolling turned wooden grip at the other. If you had a friend who could turn this item on a woodturning lathe you'd be in clover. If not, you could do it as we did the wooden drum, on a mandrel. The rough surface could be finished with a file and sandpaper while the work revolves. Cut a short piece of light alloy or brass tube for the ferrule and make it a drive fit on the end of the grip. Drive it on and polish it in situ before finishing off the turning. Try the screwed end of the handle in its socket before making the bend. You want to be sure the grip is in the right position when you assemble the handle. Mark the position of the inside of the bend with a file scratch, remove the bar to the vice, put a piece of tube over the longer portion, to give leverage, and make the bend. Silver solder a thick washer to position the grip, splay out or drill the end for a split pin, and assemble with a loose washer as shown in **Fig. 87**.

We're not going to waste your time describing the angles. Cut two pieces of angle to the specified length and drill holes as shown on the drawing **Figs. 78 & 79**. The nuts that hold the lower pillars also hold the angles in place. What more can we

Fig. 87. Alternative ways to fix the grip to the handle.

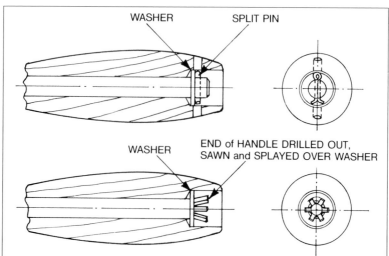

WASHER   SPLIT PIN

WASHER   END of HANDLE DRILLED OUT, SAWN and SPLAYED OVER WASHER

tell you, except that you need to make a cut-out to clear the ratchet wheel teeth? You can get the exact size of the cut by trial and error.

As regards final assembly, there's only one point we would stress, and that is to work on a flat surface when you put the winch together. It will be like putting a clock back together after you've 'mended' it, except that these pieces have never seen each other before. The gears will have been assembled to their shafts, together with the drum, so there will only be the two shaft ends to worry about. Lay the left-hand side plate down and insert the ends of all the pillars and the shafts, making sure you have them the right way around, and the longer threaded pillars are at the non-rounded bottom edge.

Lower the right-hand side plate over the pillars and shaft ends, and fit the angle; put lock washers on the pillars and run

Fig. 88. The light duty winch with its steel wire rope, thimble and shackles attached.

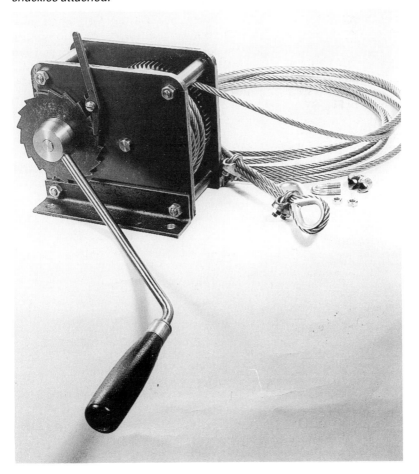

on the nuts finger tight. Stand up the assembly on its lower edges, settle it on to the flat surface and put on the left hand angle and nuts. When you're sure everything is in place and the shafts will run freely, tighten up the nuts.

Screw the ratchet plate to the handle boss, put a grubscrew into the tapped hole and slip a thin washer between the boss and the sideplate as you put the handle on its shaft. Tighten down the grubscrew. Assemble the ratchet pawl, when you're certain of its best position, with a spring and a screw into a drilled and tapped hole in the sideplate. *Et voila!* Your winch is ready to receive its cord or steel rope (**Fig. 88**).

Steel wire rope is not cheap, but you may already have some hanging around. The size and amount of rope you need will depend on what you intend doing with your winch. We imagined it in use on a small workshop crane or on the front of a flat trailer – but not to winch a boat up the slipway! Let's keep our sense of proportion.

When we designed this winch we had in mind a capacity of 5 cwts (approx 250 kg). We needed to know what rope would be best and we sought expert advice. We settled on a steel wire rope of 6 mm O/D with a 6 × 19 form and WSC. (All that means is six strands, each with 19 wires, and a wire-stranded core.) We are advised that this rope will do what we want done, but our advice to you is to check for yourself before you use any rope to lift any weight. Better safe than squashed!

10 BENCH CENTRES

Our next project (**Fig. 89**) looks like a miniature lathe. It has centres and a bed but that is where the similarity ends, because there is no way of driving the work and no provision for tools to cut it. This is a pair of bench centres which you will find useful, at some future time, for fine balancing of rotating assemblies and for checking the straightness of cylindrical work. To show you what we mean, imagine you were making a basic steam turbine – the kind we built in school from treacle tins and wire. The smooth running of the turbine rotor would depend on how well it was aligned and balanced on its shaft. These little machines run at surprisingly high speeds, and any imbalance could cause disaster. A good way of checking for balance would be to set up the rotor between the female centres, lightly gripped, with lubricant on the ends of the shaft, and spin it by hand. Let the rotor come to rest and see where it ends up. If it persists in coming to rest at the same place each time, that indicates the 'heavy' spot which must have some material removed. Keep checking and adjusting until the rotor will come to rest in any position and it will then be reasonably well balanced. This procedure is 'static' balancing; 'dynamic' balancing is more complicated and is beyond the scope of this book.

Fig. 89. The bench centres.

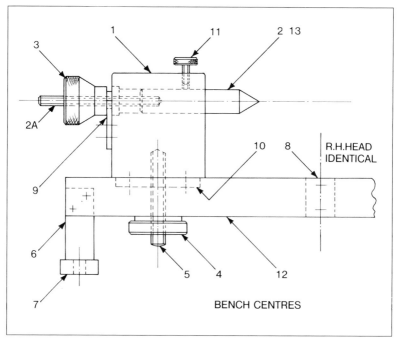

Above *Fig. 90. General arrangements (half-view) of the bench centres.*

Another function of bench centres is the checking of cylindrical work for straightness on a flat, reference, surface with the DTI.

Don't let this project's complex appearance fool you (**Figs. 90 & 91**). It is really a number of very simple parts put together to make a workmanlike machine. We begin our bench centres by making one part, adding another finished part to it and then another until we have a sub-assembly. Put three sub-assemblies together and you have the complete machine. Let's call the two sub-assemblies that carry the centres *centre heads*. Each centre head consists of nine separate parts. The bed assembly consists of seven separate parts. So the whole machine comprises 25 separate parts.

We suggest you start by making the body blocks for the centre heads. It will make more sense, we think, if you make all identical parts together. For example, the two centres with their taper-turned noses ought to be made at the same time, to avoid having to set and reset the topslide angle. Cut the two body blocks as near to length as possible and either mill or file them square and flat. Clean up all faces with emery cloth, degrease and blue the four narrow faces on each block ready for marking out. After scribing a centre line all round, the remaining marking out of the blocks should be done from the same datum face on each block. We used one of the shorter faces (**Fig. 92**) and marked each line on both blocks before changing the setting of our surface gauge.

The centre of the ⅝ in (16 mm) through-hole is quite important, and should be marked out first at both ends of the block.
Lightly centre-pop the cross lines and use the pop mark as a
centre to strike two circles on one face – ⅝ in (16 mm) and ¾ in
(19 mm) diameter – ⅝ in (16 mm) for the bore itself and ¾ in
(19 mm) for the counter bore which houses the handwheel boss
(*see* **Fig. 91**). It is vital to get the pop marks dead-on the
intersection of your scribed lines. The block will later be set to
run true in the four-jaw chuck using this pop mark.

The rest of the hole positions – all tapped holes – can then be
marked out from the drawing (**Fig. 91**) and lightly pop marked.
But once you are sure they are in the correct place – and on their
intersections – you could deepen these pop marks for drilling.
By the time the block has been in the lathe and had its bores
made, there won't be much marking blue left on any of the
faces! If the pop marks are too lightly done, they might disappear altogether. Grip the block in your four-jaw independent
chuck (**Fig. 93**) and set the centre of the long bore to run true,
using centring point and DTI. At a spindle speed of about
600 rpm start the hole with a small drill, open it out with larger
and larger drills ending up with a ³⁹⁄₆₄ in (15.5 mm) drill if you
have one. (The less metal the reamer has to remove the better
will be the finish and accuracy of the bore.) Drop the lathe
spindle speed to about 200 rpm and finish out the hole slowly
and carefully with a ⅝ in (16 mm) reamer, remembering to
withdraw the reamer slowly as well as feeding it in slowly.

Fig. 92. Marking out of the body blocks.

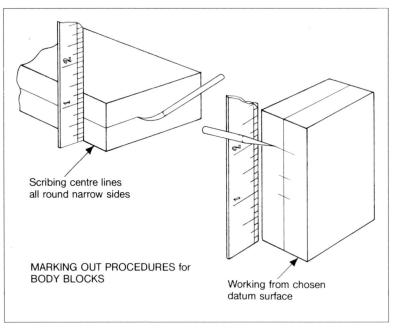

Scribing centre lines
all round narrow sides

MARKING OUT PROCEDURES for
BODY BLOCKS

Working from chosen
datum surface

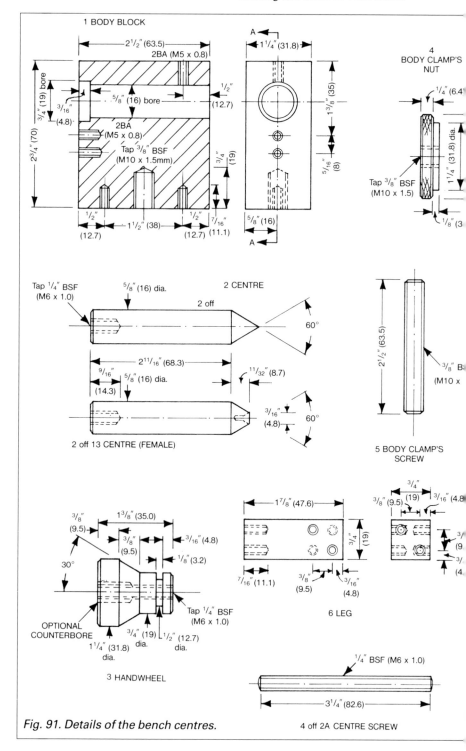

Fig. 91. Details of the bench centres.

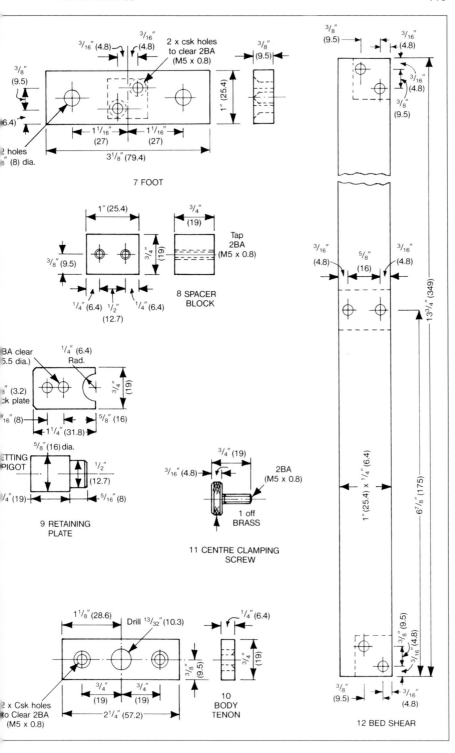

3/16" (4.8)   3/16" (4.8)   2 x csk holes to clear 2BA (M5 x 0.8)   3/8" (9.5)

3/8" (9.5)

(6.4)

2 holes 5/16" (8) dia.

1" (25.4)

1 1/16" (27)   1 1/16" (27)

3 1/8" (79.4)

7 FOOT

1" (25.4)   3/4" (19)

3/8" (9.5)   3/4" (19)

Tap 2BA (M5 x 0.8)

1/4" (6.4)   1/2" (12.7)   1/4" (6.4)

8 SPACER BLOCK

BA clear 5.5 dia.)   1/4" (6.4) Rad.

3/4" (19)

(3.2) ck plate

16" (8)   5/8" (16)

1 1/4" (31.8)

5/8" (16) dia.

ETTING PIGOT   1/2" (12.7)

/4" (19)   5/16" (8)

9 RETAINING PLATE

3/4" (19)

3/16" (4.8)   2BA (M5 x 0.8)

1 off BRASS

11 CENTRE CLAMPING SCREW

1 1/8" (28.6)   Drill 13/32" (10.3)   1/4" (6.4)

3/8" (9.5)   3/4" (19)

3/4" (19)   3/4" (19)

2 x Csk holes to Clear 2BA (M5 x 0.8)   2 1/4" (57.2)

10 BODY TENON

3/8" (9.5)   3/16" (4.8)

3/16" (4.8)   3/8" (9.5)

3/16" (4.8)   5/8" (16)   3/16" (4.8)

13 3/4" (349)

1" (25.4) x 1/4" (6.4)   6 7/8" (175)

3/8" (9.5)   3/16" (4.8)

3/8" (9.5)   3/16" (4.8)

12 BED SHEAR

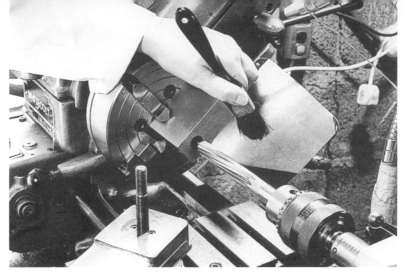

Fig. 93. Reaming the ⅝ in (16 mm) bore of the body block in a four-jaw independent chuck.

When you're satisfied with the ⅝ in (16 mm) bore, remove the drill chuck from the tailstock and push the whole thing back out of your way. Set up a small boring tool in the toolpost and adjust it to centre height. Have the tool tip projecting only far enough to cut the counterbore, which is a mere ³⁄₁₆ in (4.8 mm) deep. Too much projection will cause the tool to give out a high pitched squeal, which is hard on the nerves. On the other hand, too little projection might mean that the edge of the cross-slide crashes into the chuck jaws before the tool has a chance to do any cutting. Try it out – by hand first – at what you think is the ideal setting, to make sure everything clears everything else when the lathe is running under power.

The counterbore can be cut, using the cross-slide and topslide handwheels only, without moving the saddle. Bring the saddle up into the 'working' position, within a couple of inches of the chuck (**Fig. 94**) and check that the topslide is fully seated on its slides with no overhang. Zero the topslide with its hand wheel moving clockwise (ie, with the tool moving towards the work) and move the saddle forward until the tool point just touches the face of the block alongside the reamed hole. (If you're not sure what we mean about zeroing the topslide thimble, recap on what we said about backlash in the slide movements in Chapter 1.) With the topslide movement zeroed, lock the saddle to the bed and wind in the cross-slide so that, when you advance the topslide, the tip of the boring tool will enter the reamed hole. Now wind the cross-slide slowly out again until the cutting edge of the tool tip just contacts the inside curve of the reamed hole. Zero the cross-slide thimble, and reverse the movement of the topslide handle to withdraw the tool from the reamed hole. Put on a 30 thou (0.75 mm) cut with the cross slide handle (*ANTI-clockwise*, this time). Put the lathe speed up to about 400 rpm and you are ready to start boring. Start the lathe, wind the topslide inwards until the thimble reads 'zero' and the tool will

Fig. 94. Counterboring the body blocks.

begin cutting. Continue feeding in until the thimble tells you that you have reached a depth of ³⁄₁₆ in or 0.1875 in (4.8 mm). Withdraw the boring tool and keep repeating the whole operation until the cross-slide thimble gives the correct reading on the last cut. The counterbore should now be ¾ in (19 mm) diameter and ³⁄₁₆ in (4.8 mm) deep. Because you're winding the cross-slide handle anticlockwise you may have to arrive at the actual amount of movement by subtraction, or simply count the number of divisions moved.

The first block can now be removed from the chuck and the second one set up for boring and counterboring. Remember to wind the boring tool well out of the way of the drilling operation and put some plastic pipe over it to protect your hands. if you're using a fourway toolpost all tools not in use should be so

Fig. 95. Alignment of the centre screw in its centre, after cementing.

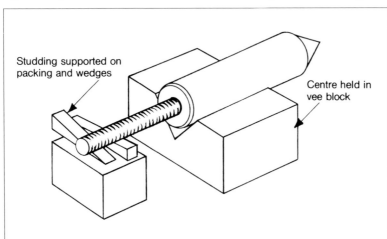

Studding supported on packing and wedges

Centre held in vee block

protected. When both blocks are bored and counterbored they can be removed to the drill press where the centre clamping screw hole and the ⅜ in BSF (M10 × 1.5 mm) hole in the base can be drilled and a start made of tapping them using the drill chuck to ensure squareness. The tapping holes for the retaining plate screws and for the tenon screws must be spotted from their components as you will see later. The tapping can be completed in the bench vice using a suitable tapwrench for the size of tap. Be especially careful when you complete the tapping of the clamping screw hole which breaks through into the ⅝ in (16 mm) bore. Never check inside the bore with your fingers. When the hole is tapped, run the ⅝ in (16 mm) reamer through the bore by hand, to remove any burrs.

We have specified silver steel for the centres (**Fig. 91**), for two reasons. In the first place, the tips of the centres must endure some knocking about. The wear they get won't be excessive, but mechanical shock might be a problem. In the second place, the centres have to slide to and fro in their body blocks and the parallel portion will have to withstand a bit of wear. BMS won't do, in our view. We would use silver steel. The procedure for making the centres is almost the same as for the centring point you made earlier. There are minor differences, however. The point *must* be made, as before, in the four-jaw chuck with the parallel part of the bar exactly concentric with the point. Unless you insist, the other end need not be so precisely held, and can be finished in the three-jaw chuck. This end is centre drilled, opened out to 5.3 mm or 5.1 mm (M6) to a depth of ⅜ in (9.5 mm) for the ¼ in BSF (M6 × 1.0 tap). The blind hole can be tapped completely in the lathe or removed and finished by hand in the vice. The 3¼ in (82.6 mm) long centre screw (**Fig. 91**) can be cut from ¼ in (6.4 mm) BMS rod, or you could use ¼ in BSF (M6 × 1.0) studding which is available not just from your model engineering supplier but from many DIY shops, too.

The end of the screw that will project beyond the handwheel, on the completed centre head, should be rounded or chamfered. The other end will be fastened into the centre either with an anaerobic adhesive or with an epoxy resin. Whichever product you use, you should make some provision for holding the screw in the correct relationship to the centre until the adhesive cures out. Vee blocks and packings might do the job (**Fig. 95**). Once fixed, the components should be left *undisturbed* overnight. Read, and comply with, the makers' instructions.

We would suggest making the retaining plates next, more to give you a little rest from lathework than for any technical reason. You could drill, saw and file these from ⅛ in (3.2 mm) thick sheet steel, using a scrap of round bar turned down to ½ in (12.7 mm) diameter as a gauge. But if you wanted to be more precise with the ½ in (12.7 mm) radius you could clamp the marked out strip to a faceplate, with packings, and bore it out. The strip could then be sawn in two to make the retaining plates.

Fig. 96. Chamfering the rear corner of a handwheel after necking it down with a parting tool.

Drill the two fixing screw holes tapping size for suitable screws and chamfer the sharp corners where appropriate. Why use tapping drills only you'll see later in the chapter. Drawfile and use emery cloth to get a good finish on these items, as they will be 'seen' at all times. The types of screw we have indicated on the drawings are only suggested. The type of head and the material it is made from is entirely up to you. If you believe dome-headed setscrews will look better – or do a better job – than socket cap screws, or vice versa, be our guest.

There's little we can say about the handwheels that we haven't already said about similar jobs in earlier chapters. This is one of those components you could make on opposite ends of the same piece of round bar. Turn them with their smaller diameters outwards (pointing away from the headstock) and complete each operation on each end before re-setting the tools. When you come to threading the centre hole, make sure you drill deeply enough with the tapping size drill so that the tapped hole extends into the section which will be taken out by the parting tool. As for the slope between the two diameters, re-cap on the method you used when you made the screw jacks in Chapter 5. Turn the smaller parallel diameter first and use the internal corner as your datum for finishing the taper. Don't forget to turn the tapered portion on both ends of the bar before you reset the angle of the topslide. The groove for the retaining plate could be cut with either a recessing tool or a parting tool of the required width or smaller. Use the retaining plate, or a scrap of the same material, as a gauge and get the best sliding fit you can. The plate shouldn't be too tight in the groove, but nor should it have more than a minimum of end play. The last operation on this component is to knurl the larger diameter before finally parting off. The procedure for knurling is detailed in Chapter 5, and after knurling we suggest that you chamfer the outer corner before going in too deeply with the parting tool.

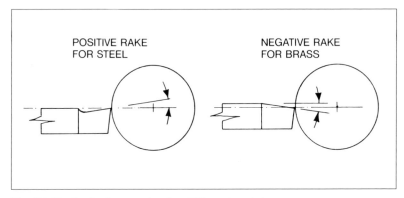

Fig. 97. Tool grinding angles for different metals.

Feed in the parting tool for about ³⁄₁₆ in (4.8 mm), bring up the chamfering tool, cut a 30 thou (0.76 mm) chamfer on the rear corner of the handwheel (**Fig. 96**) and then part off.

The things we said earlier, about the centre screw, apply equally to the body clamping screw except that this is a ³⁄₈ in BSF (M10 × 1.5) thread and its length is 2½ in (63.5 mm). Whichever way you choose, take the same care as you did with the centre screws to position the screw at right angles to the base in both planes before the adhesive begins to set. Do not disturb for at least 12hr or better still leave it alone overnight. One of the secrets of successful use of engineering adhesives is to thoroughly degrease the parts beforehand, using a suitable solvent. When degreasing components we use only clean paper towels or tissues and dispose of them at once, so that the grease we've so carefully removed doesn't get carried back on to the surfaces.

The body clamping nut and the centre clamping screw are straightforward turning jobs. The similarities with other parts you have made will enable you quickly to work out the best procedure for making them. The centre clamping screw is to be made from brass and we should point out one or two things about this material before we go any further. Brass is softer than steel, easier to cut and takes a brilliant finish from the tool without your needing emery cloth. The cutting angles of turning tools for brass are not quite the same as for steel (**Fig. 97** tells you what these differences are) but if you are careful, the 'steel' tools will do the job adequately. Some workers claim that coolant or cutting oil is unnecessary for turning brass, but others use coolant nonetheless. For small, simple jobs our choice would be to work dry. Ask around, get all the advice you can, and make up your own mind. Eye protection is a must when working brass. The swarf comes off at high speed in the form of needles which can be very destructive of human tissues!

You should have quite a heap of finished parts by now and we're sure you'll be eager to get on with a trial assembly, but there are one or two important procedures to learn before we get that far. Look at the body tenon for instance. It looks quite simple – just a strip of BMS flat with three holes in it. But there's more to it than meets the eye. If we had gone ahead at an early stage and drilled and tapped the body block, then marked out and drilled the tenon – all from the drawings – we might have been lucky. The tenon's sides *might* have lined up exactly with the bed shears and the edges of the body base. But if we had screwed the tenon in place and discovered it didn't line up, what could we have done about it? The screw holes are countersunk. Have you ever tried relocating a countersunk hole? If you have, you will know that it's a humiliating task.

Do not despair! Here's a way to get your parts to line up consistently and to a high degree of accuracy. Begin with the tenons. Cut them to length and file their ends reasonably square with their sides before blueing and marking out. The centre hole, the one which clears the 3/8 in BSF (M10) screw, can be drilled ¹³⁄₃₂ in (10.3 mm) – its finished size – right away. The other two holes are different. You should drill them *tapping* size only, at this stage – 4 mm for 2BA, 4.2 mm for M5 × 0.8 thread – then you're ready for the next operation. When you made the two retaining plates, you will remember you drilled them tapping-size for their fixing screws too. The reason for all this will now become clear.

Place one of the tenons in position on the base, with packing strips to locate it parallel with the sides of the body block, and clamp it tightly with toolmakers clamps or something similar. Use clamps which leave you enough room to get the assembly under the chuck of your drill press. Drill the tapping holes, using

Fig. 98. The spigot being used to align a retaining plate for spotting through.

the holes in the tenon as a jig. If you're measuring the depth from the top surface, remember to add on the thickness of the tenon. Repeat the process for the other tenon. We'd like to say 'repeat the process' for the retaining plates, but there's a snag. These plates have to have the centre of the semicircular cut-out aligned with the centre of the handwheel and we need a way to set this up with confidence. Our solution was to use a setting spigot (**Fig. 98**) with a ⅝ in (16 mm) diameter and a ½ in (12.7 mm) diameter, made from a scrap end of bar. With the spigot placed in the counterbored end of the bore and its ½ in (12.7 mm) dia projecting, the plate can be positioned and clamped down. This way you *know* it will be in the right place. Spot the holes through the plates, as you did for the tenon and drill them to the correct depth with the required tapping drill for your chosen screws.

The body tapping can now be completed, and the holes in the tenons and the retaining plates opened out with the necessary clearing-sized drills. If you are using cap screws to secure the retaining plates, they will not need any further work. The tenons must be held with countersunk screws to clear the top of the bed legs and so you should countersink them to suit the heads of your chosen screws. Now you can do a trial assembly of your two centre heads. Don't tighten any of the screws more than finger-tight; you may have slight adjustments to make when you come to assemble the heads to the bed.

The bed! There is no lathework to do on this part of the project, unless you want to be really ambitious and turn a pair of

Fig. 99. The centre pop mark code to reposition parts after dismantling.

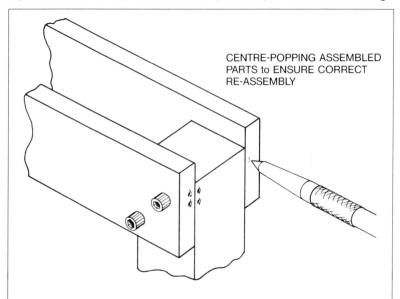

CENTRE-POPPING ASSEMBLED PARTS to ENSURE CORRECT RE-ASSEMBLY

feet in place of the squarish ones shown in the drawing (**Fig. 91**). We're going to assume you've decided against that, and describe the construction of the bed as drawn. The procedure throughout, for the positioning of the tapped holes, is the same as it was for those of the tenons and retaining plates. The two bed shears could be clamped together, marked out and drilled tapping-size to suit your screw threads, as though they were one piece of bar. Cut the feet and the spacer block from ¾ in (19 mm) square material and file the ends square. This is important, and care should be taken to check the squareness of the ends of both the feet and the spacer block with an engineers' square on a reliable flat surface.

The tapped holes in the legs, for the screws holding on the feet, are deep enough to take screws ¾ in (19 mm) long. The feet themselves are marked out and the ⁵⁄₁₆ in (8 mm) fixing holes drilled first. The other two holes in each foot are drilled tapping-size for the fixing screws. Clamp the feet to the legs to spot the tapping holes through, and do the same with the legs, the spacer block and the bed shears to spot through the remaining tapping holes. This is where the squareness of all the ¾ in (19 mm) square parts becomes vital. While you have the components clamped together, mark some of the junctions with pop-mark patterns (**Fig. 99**) so that all will go back together in the right order after drilling. When all holes are spotted through, the parts can be released from the clamps and the tapping finished. With clearance holes opened out in the shears and feet, the bed parts are ready for assembly on a flat surface, working by your pop-mark code. Put everything together lightly at first. Tighten all screws finger tight, and try the bed shears upside down on the flat surface. Test for wobble and check all faces with a square before pinching up the screws a little.

Now turn it right-way-up and try the centre heads in position between the shears. Don't screw them to the shears just yet. Sight along the length of the bed to see whether the blocks are in line. Make any small adjustments by tapping the structure at the appropriate point with a brass or rawhide hammer. Slide the centre heads to and fro to ensure that the tenons don't bind on the top of either leg. When you're satisfied, tighten everything up finally.

We need an alternative pair of centres for our machine – ones with a depression in the end instead of a 60° point (**Fig. 90**). These are our female centres and they have a centre hole, with a top diameter of about ³⁄₁₆ in (4.8 mm) as well as the usual 60° slope. It is the centre hole which does the gripping, in this instance, or you could have a male centre at one end and a female centre at the other, as you would if you wanted to mount a centring point between them. If you provide yourself with both types you'll be prepared for virtually any balancing or inspection job. In the next chapter we're going to set intellectual things aside, for a time, and concentrate on a bit of brute force.

11 TOGGLE PUNCH

We're going to talk about the relationship between eccentric turning and the problems of making holes in sheet metal. You've all had experience of trying to put a round hole through a piece of thin metal – when the drill snaps off short just as you're going to break through, or the metal 'snatches' and bends itself double. Even if none of these things happen, you still end up with a hole that's more triangular than circular. In any 'thinnish' material the professionals don't bother with twist drills. They bang the hole through with a punch-and-die set.

In Chapter 3 you made the eccentric, which is at the heart of the machine we're going to build next, the toggle punch (**Fig. 100**). Picture, if you will, a steam engine. They usually have a piston, working in a cylinder, driving a connecting rod attached to a crank which, in turn, drives the flywheel. The toggle punch is similar in its outward appearance, except that we have an eccentric instead of the crank and the whole thing works backwards. We apply force on the handle which rotates the

Fig. 100. The toggle punch, punching 16 SWG (1.63 mm) aluminium.

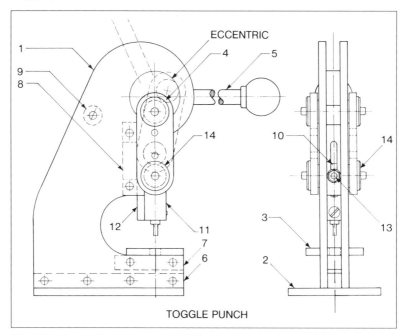

ECCENTRIC

TOGGLE PUNCH

Fig. 101. General arrangement of the toggle punch.

eccentric (**Fig. 101**). The links attached to the eccentric are coupled to a slider which moves between guides. This means that the slider, and the punch held in its nose, moves down or up as we move the handle. The secret of this toggle action is that when the eccentric pins reach almost the lowest point of their travel they are exerting increased thrust on the punch. When the pins near bottom dead centre their force is at a maximum – just the right point at which to punch a hole in metal. It's rather like heaving on the flywheel of a steam engine in order to crack a walnut under the piston (**Fig. 102**).

Study the general arrangement drawing (**Fig. 101**) and the detail drawings (**Figs. 103 & 104**) with care. Most of the labour involved goes into marking out, cutting plates and bar to size, drilling and tapping. The only bits of serious lathework are the handle, the thrust block, the punch, the links and the washers. We'll tell you about them in detail, and simply sketch out the procedures for the rest of the components. True, we will bore out the eccentric bearings in the lathe with a boring head, but we're not sure that qualifies as proper lathework.

You will remember the square material we used for the instrument maker's vice knuckles in Chapter 7, and the method we used to hold it in the chuck. The thrust block is a similar case, and the same procedure can be used. Measure the distance across the corners of ¾ in (19 mm) square bar and make a split sleeve (you could call it a collet) to suit. Cut a piece of this square

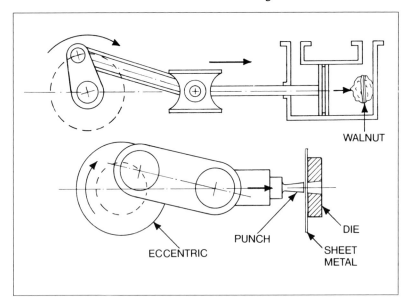

WALNUT

DIE

PUNCH

ECCENTRIC

SHEET
METAL

Above *Fig. 102. The 'steam engine' analogy.*

Right *Fig. 103. Details of the toggle punch.*

bar 1⅝ in (41.3 mm) long, and grip it in the three-jaw chuck with your collet. Turn each end to ¾ in (19 mm) diameter for a length of ⁹⁄₃₂ in (7.1 mm) face and drill tapping size for a 2BA (M5 × 0.8) tapped hole. You can please yourself whether you just start the tapping in the lathe or do the whole job before removing it from the chuck. Another way of tackling this would be to centre drill the ends only, and complete drilling and tapping in the drill press. There is a lot of other drilling and tapping to do on the parts of the slider, so it makes sense to do it with as little moving around as possible.

Clean, degrease and blue the required faces of the thrust block. Mark out the hole positions as shown in **Fig. 104**, and set it aside for the moment while you get out a piece of ¾ in (19 mm) square bar 1³⁄₁₆ in (30.2 mm) long for the punch ram. Put this in the collet, grip it in the chuck and face both ends. The upper end-face is where the ram will be fixed to the thrust block (**Fig. 104**). The lower end must be faced and centre drilled before opening out to ⁵⁄₁₆ in (8 mm) diameter and ¹⁹⁄₃₂ (15 mm) deep to receive the shank of a punch. Prepare for marking out the various holes but, before you start drilling, let us explain something.

Many of the holes you will drill over the next 100 years or so will be for assembly fastenings of one kind or another. They are usually made in pairs – perhaps a tapped hole in the component and a clearance hole in the part which is to be held to it. If you're bolting one part to another it may be that both holes are of

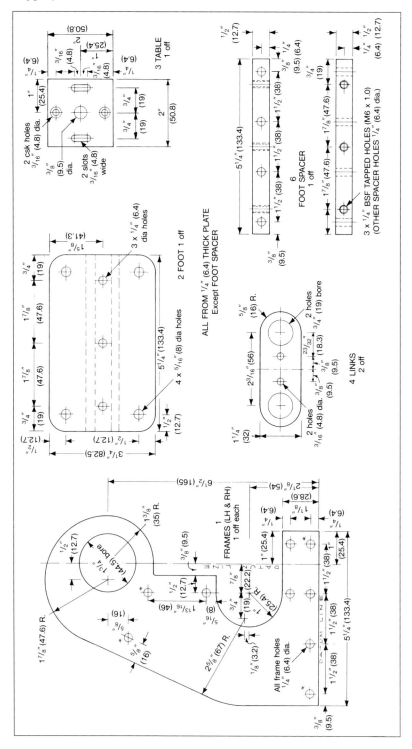

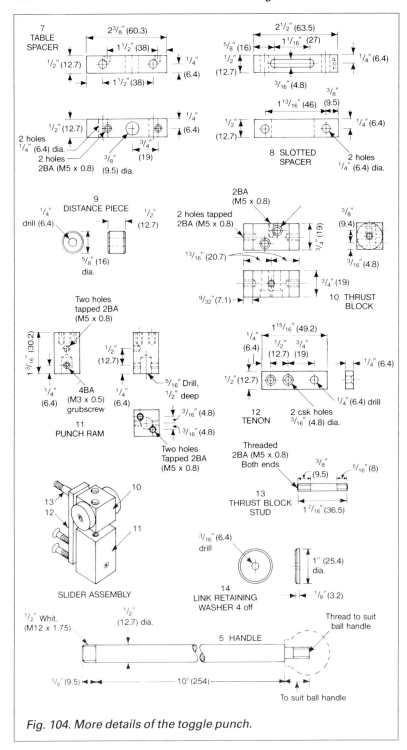

Fig. 104. More details of the toggle punch.

clearance size, that is big enough to let a bolt shank pass right through. Then you'll have the bolt head on one side of the assembly and a washer and nut on the other. If both holes are clearance holes, no problem! But if one set of holes is clearance size and the corresponding set is tapped, you have to be more cautious. We've gone into this briefly in the previous chapter.

Let's take the assembly of the thrust block to the punch ram as an example. There are two tapped holes on the head of the ram corresponding with two counterbored holes in the thrust block. The thrust block pair are shown counterbored to take the heads of socket cap screws (**Fig. 104**). Drill the holes in the thrust block first, but *don't* drill them clearance size, drill them *tapping* size. Now you can clamp the thrust block to the head of the ram and gently spot the holes through with the same drill. SPOT them only, mind, don't try to drill them to full depth at this stage. Separate the two pieces, complete the tap drilling and start the thread in the drill press. Last of all, open out the holes in the thrust block to clearance size and counterbore them to suit the cap screws. Using this procedure, you'll have more certainty that the two components are going to match up when you finally tighten up the screws.

At the back of the punch ram/thrust block assembly is a tenon which slides between the plates and keeps the punch on course as it travels downwards. Use the technique we've just outlined to drill the holes in these parts, to fix the tenon in place. The thrust block stud (**Fig. 101**) passes through a clearance hole in the tenon and into a tapped hole in the thrust block.

The handle is a simple piece of threading with little actual turning involved, unless the outer end has to be reduced to suit the type of knob you choose. ½ in Whitworth is a big thread (M14 × 2.0 mm) and will probably be better accomplished in the small lathe by using a diestock (and the tailstock barrel for

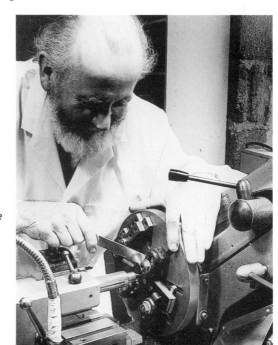

Fig. 105. Harold taps the links with a brass strip to set them true on the faceplate. Note the ¼ in (6.4 mm) packings under the links.

support) than by trying to do it with a travelling dieholder. Our way was to cut an 11 in (280 mm) length of ½ in (12.7 mm) dia BMS bar and reduce the diameter at one end for threading to suit a plastic knob. The other end was threaded to match the ½ in Whitworth (M14) socket in the eccentric, and the bit in between was polished up with fine emery to a smart finish.

Deciding how to machine the two links gave us a problem or two. We could have made them separately and depended on the accuracy of our marking out to get the centres of the two pairs of ¾ in (19 mm) holes the same. We could equally well have used the milling machine table movements to position the centres for us, and spotted them with a centre drill. But we plumped for doing the whole thing on the faceplate of the lathe and ensuring accuracy by bolting the links together for drilling and boring (**Fig. 105**). That's what the two ³⁄₁₆ in (4.8 mm) diameter holes are for, if you've been wondering. You could always plug them by pressing in short pieces of rod. Personally we think they add character to the punch, so we left them as they are.

Saw yourself two 3½ in (89 mm) lengths of 1¼ in × ¼ in (32 mm × 6.4 mm) BMS flat for your links and blue one of them for marking out. Scribe a centre line down its length, find the mid-point and mark it with a short cross-line. Set a pair of small dividers to ⅜ in (9.5 mm) and step off this distance on each side of the mid-point. These two marks are the centres for the ³⁄₁₆ in (4.8 mm) holes as shown in the drawing (**Fig. 103**). Reset the dividers to 1³⁄₃₂ in (27.7 mm) and step of, as before, to mark the centres of the ¾ in (19 mm) diameter holes. Check, once more, that these two centres are 2³⁄₁₆ in (55.6 mm) apart before you lightly spot all the centre positions with a centre punch. Scribe circles and semicircles to show the finished sizes of the ¾ in (19 mm) holes and the radius at the end of the link. When you have peered at them all through a magnifying glass, and you're sure they are where they're supposed to be, deepen the two outer pop marks a little, because we'll be using these for setting up on the faceplate.

Now clamp the links together, temporarily to drill ³⁄₁₆ in (4.8 mm) holes at the two middle positions and find a pair of screws and nuts, complete with washers, to suit. Release the clamps and screw the link blanks securely together, checking that the sides are perfectly aligned, and clamp them to the faceplate on ¼ in (6.4 mm) packings as shown in **Fig. 105**. Note the counterbalancing pieces attached to the faceplate to cut down vibration when the whole assembly is spinning at 200 rpm. We know 200 rpm doesn't seem very fast, but when you have a pound or so (half-a-kilo) of metal fixed well away from the centre of a biggish faceplate and it's all running at this speed, the effects can be quite instructive. *Don't try it* unless you are sure your lathe is *securely* fastened down.

There are several ways in which you can set up the centre pops on the links for drilling. You can use the DTI and pump centre finder, as we did in Chapter 10 and earlier, or you could use a wiggler and the power of the human eye (*Chapter 8*, **Fig. 73**). We decided we'd do it the simple way and bring up the tailstock with a dead centre in the socket. When you position the point of the centre so that it doesn't quite touch the work, it is easy to see where, and by how much, you need to make adjustment. Don't clamp the links too tightly to the faceplate at this stage. When the point of the dead centre goes into the pop mark, tighten everything up. Replace the centre with your centre drill holder or tailstock drill chuck, check everything clears the work and begin the process of drilling and opening out the hole.

The sequence we used was centre drill first, followed by ⅛ in (3.2 mm), ⁵⁄₁₆ in (8 mm), ½ in (12.7 mm) and ²³⁄₃₂ in (18.3 mm) drills, finishing out the hole to ¾ in (19 mm) with a boring tool. When you have the holes almost to size, measure frequently and – finally – use the ¾ in (19 mm) diameters you've already turned as gauges. With these diameters an easy sliding fit in the links, you are ready to release the workpieces from the faceplate clamps, turn the assembly end-for-end and carry out the same operations on the other end. When this sequence is complete your links will have their ¾ in (19 mm) holes bored to suit both the thrust block and the eccentric, and their centres will be exactly the same distance apart. This will ensure that the force from the handle will be applied equally to the two ends of the thrust block.

The thrust block stud (**Fig. 104**) is a piece of ³⁄₁₆ in (4.8 mm) dia BMS rod threaded as shown on the detail drawing (**Fig. 103**). You could cut these easily with dies in your travelling dieholder. Find a suitable nut and a thick washer with an outside diameter that will fit between the frames, run the nut on to one end of the stud, pop the washer on and screw the stud loosely into the thrust block. This is just to save you searching for the bits and pieces when final assembly time arrives. We're not going to say much about the link retaining washers. Look at the drawings (**Figs. 103 & 104**), get out some 1 in (25.4 mm) dia BMS bar and get busy! You could use a 2½ in (63.5 mm) length of bar, remembering that one inch (25.4 mm) bar won't go through the spindle, and cut all the washers off one end. If you are a little apprehensive about parting off at that distance from the chuck jaws, you could use two shorter lengths – say 1¾ in (44.5 mm) – and cut two washers from each piece. Put a nice finish on the outsides of the washers – they'll be in full view and attract lots of attention when you operate your toggle punch for the pleasure of visitors to your workshop.

To punch holes you'll need a toolset, and a toolset consists of a punch and its matching die (**Fig. 106**). The shank of the punch goes into the punch ram and the die is fixed to the table, but we'll talk about that later. We make our punch out of a 1¼ in (31.8 mm) length of ⁵⁄₁₆ in (8 mm) dia silver steel. It doesn't seem exacting, until you notice that the drawing (**Fig. 103**) calls

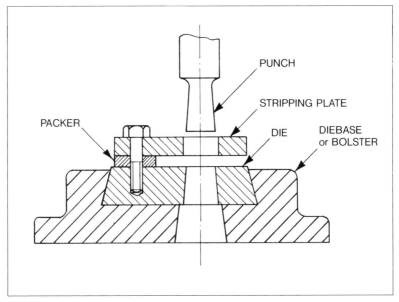

PUNCH

STRIPPING PLATE

PACKER

DIE   DIEBASE
         or BOLSTER

Fig. 106. A punch and die toolset for punching thicker steel plates.

for a taper of just 1° on each side of the punch diameter. This is, in effect, a relief angle which does the same job as those on your cutting tools in stopping the cut surface from rubbing against the tool.

Actually tapering the punch is no problem. All you have to do is nudge over the topslide to one degree out of alignment with the lathe axis, and do all your turning with the topslide handwheel. The punch itself should be hardened and tempered to a pale straw colour at the tip. What heat treatment you apply to the die will depend on what material you choose. We used high carbon steel plate from a surplus supplier, and it has worked very well (so far) without any heat treatment. If we were intending using the machine to punch steel all the time, of course we'd need to consider heat treating the tooling. In that event we'd go back to our supplier and throw ourselves on his mercy.

The frames and the foot **(Fig. 103)** are made from ¼ in (6.4 mm) thick hot rolled steel plate, which has a uniform grey scale surface, resistant to scribing. We coated the plate with white opaque marking out fluid, marked out with carbide scribers and flame-cut the frames to the line with oxy-acetylene equipment. If you don't have such luxurious facilities, we're afraid you'll have to do this job the hard way. Saw to the line where you can, and drill closely space holes in areas where sawing is not practicable. Sawing and filing will get you there eventually. Tension files are excellent for cutting to curved lines, but the technique needs care and patience if you are not to spend your days tripping to and from the toolshop for new blades. Make a neat draw-filed job of the edges because, except for the two bottom edges, they'll all be on view. Those of you who own vertical milling machines will already have worked out your plan of campaign for 'nibbling' round those edges with an end-mill.

Only one frame should be marked out for bolt holes and these should be drilled next with the correct clearance size drill for the bolts you intend using. Find your bolts and nuts first. Clamp the two frames firmly together and spot through four of the drilled holes into the lower plate. Pick hole positions such as the ones starred on the drawing (**Fig. 103**) (remembering that the next operation is to bore out the eccentric bearing holes) and bolt the frames securely together with four bolts, nuts and washers. It is essential to make sure the base edges and the edges which will support the punch table are exactly in line before tightening up the nuts. If they did not coincide, the axis of the eccentric could be forced out of line at the assembly stage.

We used the set-up shown in **Fig. 107** to carry out the boring operation, using a small precision boring head in the headstock spindle nose and an angle plate bolted to the cross-slide boring table. As you can see, the topslide assembly was removed to give us more room and the spigot hole was plugged to keep swarf out of the works. The handbook for your lathe will show you how to do it on your lathe, but ask around too, to find out how other people do it. We found the centre pop mark with a solid centre in the spindle nose (**Fig. 107**), clamped the plates firmly, and began by centre drilling and working up in stages to the biggest size drill we own, 23 mm (0.906 in) diameter.

Remember to check the spindle speed each time you change up to a larger drill. By the time we reached 23 mm (0.906 in) diameter we had dropped into fastest backgear speed (80 rpm). When we're drilling we tend to rely on the evidence of our ears to decide what speed we ought to be using. If there is an unholy

Fig. 107. Finding the centre of the eccentric bearing holes in the frames.

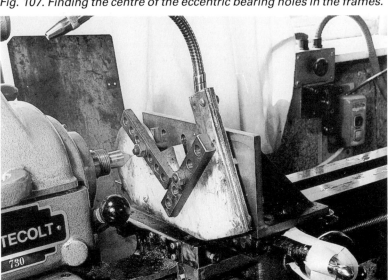

scream when drill meets metal, we take this as a warning that we're going too fast, even though the 'speeds' graph (**Fig. 11**) says we can run at 400 rpm with a 23 mm (0.906 in) diameter BMS workpiece. *JUDGEMENT* is the name of the game! Our next job was to get out our precision boring head and fit it with a short cutter bar to reduce overhang (**Fig. 108**). We started cutting at a very slow speed and worked up until we were getting thick swarf without undue squealing from the tool point. When we were near to finished size, we used the eccentric to gauge the bore until it was a good sliding fit all the way through both frames.

Remove the bored frames from the angle plate, take off the angle plate, clean down the boring table and put the topslide back in its working position. Knock out the boring head, clean it, and put it back into storage. With the frames still bolted together, drill all the remaining bolt holes through the lower plate. Separate the frames, deburr all the edges that need it and set the frames aside for a minute, while we saw out all the ½ in (12.7 mm) square spacers.

Clamp the spacers in their respective positions on one frame and spot through the bolt holes with the clearance-size drill. But before you release the clamps, mark the spacers with a scriber or centre punch code so that they all go back the right way round after drilling. Clamp the frames together again, drill all the holes and deburr them on both sides so that the burrs can't prevent the frames bedding down properly when they're bolted. The foot spacer has three tapped holes and it also needs a ³⁄₁₆ in (4.8 mm) deep rebate taken out on its top face for a distance of

Fig. 108. An early stage in boring out the bearing holes with a precision boring head.

1⅜ in (35 mm) from the front end. We didn't show this on the drawing to avoid clutter. This can be sawn and filed or milled, but watch out for the horizontal bolt hole! This rebate is to provide an exit for the punchings from beneath the table. The table spacer has a ⅜ in (9.5 mm) diameter hole which corresponds with the hole in the centre of the table.

The slotted spacer, as its name implies, has a slot to accommodate the thrust block stud. This can be milled, or close-drilled and sawn, to give the stud enough clearance for easy movement up and down. Deburr the edges of the slot as you did for the bolt holes. The foot will be needed next, so clean up its edges and round the corners as shown on the drawings. Drill the holding down holes ⁵⁄₁₆ in (8 mm) diameter and three tapping size holes along the longer centre line, for securing to the foot spacer, these will be opened out later to ¼ in (6.4 mm) diameter and countersunk deeply on the underside to take countersunk machine screws. The three holes can then be spotted on the underside of the spacer, and the spacer drilled and tapped. Ours were ¼ in BSF (M6 × 1.0)

The only piece left to make now is the table. We made ours from a 2 in (50.8 mm) length of 2 in (50.8 mm) × ¼ in (6.4 mm) bright steel, which was easily blued and marked out for the holes and slots. Drill the countersunk holes first with the tapping drill, and spot them through on to the table spacer. Drill and tap the spacer, open out the screw holes in the table and countersink them to suit the screws. Keep the heads a few thou (hundredths of a millimetre) below the table surface. Drill the ⅜ in (9.5 mm) diameter hole in the centre, drill and cut the slots, which are intended for fastening down tooling on the table, suitable packed up to meet the punch. Slots in the dieplate, at right angles to those in the table, will give you plenty of scope for adjustment.

Now it is time to do a trial assembly. Bolt everything together, finger tight at first, remembering to attach the foot spacer to the foot before adding the frame, and insert the eccentric into its bearing holes before fitting the handle. Do not fasten anything finally at this stage. Add the links and their retaining washers, put a punch into the nose socket of the ram and all is – almost – ready. We made a temporary die plate for trial purposes and screwed it in place on the table after trying the punch tip for alignment with the hole. Try your punch on something easy, like aluminium of about 16g (1.63 mm or 0.064 in) and you'll get a great thrill out of hearing it *'zonk'* through the metal. The neatness of the resulting hole makes all your labour worthwhile and we're sure you'll start at once to think up all the different tooling you can make for your toggle punch. But don't get too involved! We want you to think about circular spacing of holes and flats and how to get it exactly the same all the way round. The indexing fixture in the next chapter will make it child's play.

12 INDEXING FIXTURE

If you've been doing the background reading we suggest at the end of the book, by now you'll have heard about indexing and dividing attachments for the lathe. You really only need a dividing head or a dividing attachment if you are looking forward to the day when you can cut your own gear teeth or graduate your own micrometer thimbles. If you are, more power to your elbow. But the vast majority of our jobs don't call for your all-singing-all-dancing dividing equipment. What they do call for is a simple – even rudimentary – indexing fixture, and that's what we're going to make next (**Fig. 109**).

It will enable you to cut squares and hexagons on the end of round bars, to space out screw holes on a pitch circle without prior marking-out, to cut the flutes on pin drills and milling cutters – the list is endless! Meanwhile, there's metal to be cut!

First, you'll need a piece of 1 in (25.4 mm) dia BMS bar 6½ in (165 mm) long for the spindle, and two pieces of ¾ in × 1¼ in (19 mm × 31.8 mm) flat, each 2¾ in (70 mm) long, for the pillars. The base plate is made from 1⅝ in × ⅜ in (41.3 × 9.5 mm) BMS flat and is 6 in (152.4 mm) long. If you get all these materials out at the beginning, you can decide for

Fig. 109. The basic indexing fixture. The slots shown on the drawings have been lengthened for more versatility.

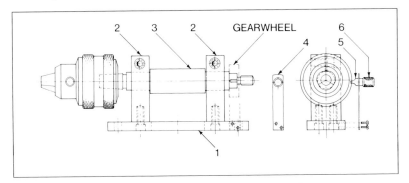

Fig. 110. General arrangement of the basic indexing fixture.

yourself what order of machining you're going to adopt. At this stage you should have sufficient experience in sorting out logical and efficient ways of proceeding with projects, but we'll drop you some hints and leave the final decisions to you.

Take the spindle as an example. (**Figs. 110 & 111**) you could set it up between centres and turn the whole thing, taper nose, seating for gear, and ⅜ in BSF (M10 × 1.5 mm) thread included, at one set-up. Gauging the taper might be a little awkward and some may look on screwcutting this size of thread as work-for-work's-sake, but you'd have the consolation of guaranteed concentricity. Do we need guaranteed concentricity? Opinions will differ and, as we said, it's up to you to decide. We decided concentricity was quite important for this particular device and turned all our diameters between centres. The threading and taper cutting were done in the four-jaw chuck. The routine for turning the taper was the same as for the morse taper in Chapter 4, except that we used the arbor socket of a drill-chuck as a gauge.

Here's another decision to make. Do we make the pillars first and gauge the ¾ in (19 mm) diameters with their bores? Or do we make the spindle first and gauge the pillar bores with the bearing diameters? It depends whether you believe it's better to do it one way than the other. There are many things to be said for each method. Our decision was made on the grounds that we own a ¾ in (19 mm) dia reamer. We made the pillars first, faced off both ends of them in the four-jaw, drilled and bored the bearing holes to within 20 thou (0.5 mm) and ran the reamer through them to bring them to size. We were then able to use the pillars to gauge the bearing diameters, knowing the holes were parallel (**Fig. 112**). Drill tapping size holes above the bearings and counterbore to suit your chosen hexagon socket cap screws. Open out with a clearing size drill but only take it in halfway, as we did for the knuckles and collet clamp on the instrument maker's vice in Chapter 7. This will leave the clearance hole on one side of the ³⁄₃₂ in (2.4 mm) slit, and the tapped hole on the other. The slit can be hacksawn or cut with a slitting

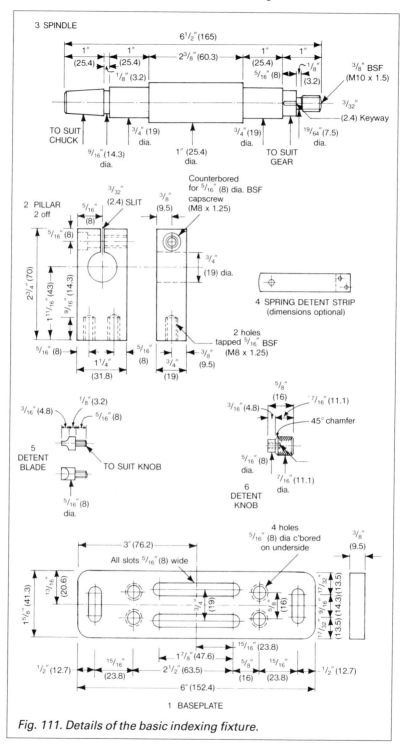

Fig. 111. Details of the basic indexing fixture.

saw of the right thickness. Ignore the two tapped holes in the foot of each pillar for the moment, they'll be spotted through later from the baseplate.

Clean up the baseplate, get it to correct length with neat radiused corners, degrease and blue it. We marked out the holes and the slots and indicated the position of the pillars with lightly scribed lines. We thought if we drilled the pillar fixing holes first, we could use them to fasten down the baseplate for milling the slots. If you intend drilling and sawing out the slots this won't be important and you can do the whole lot together. You'll notice that the slots shown in the drawings are longer than those in the photograph. This was done to make the fixture fit more machines. There isn't much argument about the best way to present the pillars to the baseplate for spotting through. We took the obvious course, clamping the pillars to the spindle with capscrews, with their bases on a flat surface, before securing them in the right place on the baseplate for spotting (**Fig. 113**). Mark their relationship to each other with a centre pop code, as before, and take them off the spindle again for full drilling and tapping. Finish off the holes in the baseplate by opening them out and counterboring to suit the fixing screws, deburr everything and set it aside.

There is a keyway to cut on the gearwheel diameter of the spindle, or you could use the 'headless screw' technique we suggested for the winch shafts in Chapter 9. Whichever method you use must give the change gear an immoveable grip on the spindle. This is the essence of the indexing fixture – that all parts remain in the same fixed relationship to each other throughout indexing movements. If they don't, you'll get rhomboids instead of squares and polygons instead of hexagons.

While we're talking about fixing the change wheel, let's look at the alternatives. We have featured a 24-toothed gear wheel,

Fig. 112. Using the reamed hole in a pillar to gauge the ¾ in (19 mm) bearing diameter on the spindle.

Fig. 113. Pillars clamped to the spindle by their own clamping screws for spotting through from the underside of the baseplate.

which was extra to the changewheel set that came with our lathe. To find out what divisions you can get with a given number of teeth, factorise the number. A 6-tooth gear, such as the bull-wheel on the headstock of a Myford Super 7 lathe, is often quoted as being ideal for indexing purposes. It's teeth factorise as follows: 2, 3 and 5. These are useful numbers – we can already get a square (4), a hexagon (6), and spanner flats (2). From the basic factors we can also get larger numbers of accurate divisions, such as 10, 12, 15, 20, and 30. All you need to know is whether the number of divisions you want will divide without a remainder into the number of teeth available.

Although the commercial dividing heads use a disc with rings of holes, the principle is the same. If the convenience of plates, with several rings of holes at different spacings, appeals to you, read up about them. You may decide to modify our design to use drilled division plates instead of gears. Some people may look askance at us for using a solid spindle, but coming at this stage in the career of a newcomer to the art, it is quite complex enough. Ambitious readers may want to look at the advantages of a hollow spindle, but be warned! Every expansion of your horizons brings a new crop of problems to be solved. We hope you'll agree with us that the love of problem-solving is what separates humans from vegetables.

You'll notice we've been a bit vague about sizes and material for the detent strip, for the simple reason that we found our piece in the scrap box. It's a piece of ⅜ in × 16 SWG (9.5 mm × 1.63 mm) hard brass. Be careful and check that your piece isn't in the 'glass-hard' condition, which means you can't drill it. It could be made out of spring steel or manganese bronze. Find something which is in the annealed or 'soft' state then, if it's spring steel, you can harden and temper it, when you've drilled the holes for the detent and for the fixing screws into the bedplate. Clamp the spring to the bedplate and spot through for the tapping holes. We haven't specified screws; ours came from surplus stocks. Find something close to those shown on the drawings (**Fig. 110**).

The detent knob is another item for which our design is merely a suggestion. You may prefer spherical knobs or plain turned ones – please yourself, so long as it looks good when it's finished. The detent blade must be shaped to fit tightly between the teeth of the gear with no rattle when the spring is fully engaged (**Fig. 114**) – rattle means clearance, clearance allows movement and movement leads to sloppy spacing. If you've voted to use discs, you will need to redesign the detent arrangement to suit, but we'll leave you to grapple with that one!

Let's assume you've had no divergent ideas, for the moment, and you've done everything according to the drawings. Now's the time to try your indexing fixture together and find out what it can do.

Slip the pillars on to the spindle according to the centre pop marks, clamp them lightly, tap the chuck firmly on to its taper, offer up the assembly to the baseplate and screw it down with all four cap screws. Now release the spindle clamping screws and check the spindle for free movement. Add a couple of spots of light machine oil in the required places and rotate the spindle to distribute the oil to the bearings.

Tap the gear over its key and on to its seating and secure with a nut and washer. Add the detent assembly last of all, and bend the spring, as necessary, to make the blade engage the tooth spaces of the gear in a satisfactory manner. All it needs now is a test-run. Grip a short piece of, say, ⅝ in (16 mm) round bar in

Fig. 114. The importance of correct shaping of the detent blade.

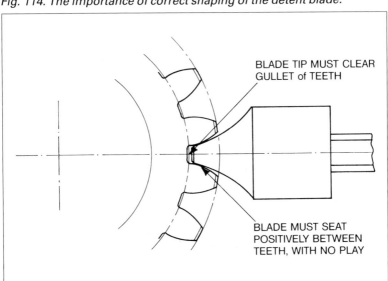

BLADE TIP MUST CLEAR GULLET of TEETH

BLADE MUST SEAT POSITIVELY BETWEEN TEETH, WITH NO PLAY

Fig. 115. The indexing fixture set up on the lathe to mill a hexagon head on a piece of bar. Note the endmill held in a milling cutter holder, and the spigot hole for the topslide stopped up to keep out swarf.

the chuck and fasten down the fixture on the lathe boring table or the milling machine table. If the centre-height of your lathe brings the lathe axis above the spindle centre of your indexing fixture you only need to pack up the base to bring the work where you want it. If the fixture centreline is above the lathe axis, try using it on an angle plate with the pillars lying horizontally. You should have plenty of scope for adjustments this way. Grip a milling cutter in the three-jaw or in a taper shank cutter holder in the mandrel nose. Check the lathe speed with the graph (**Fig. 11**) and feed the work on to the cutter with the cross-slide handle. The cut is made and the spindle is moved the required number of teeth before making the next cut (**Fig. 115**). You have to develop a routine for this type of operation, just as you did for screwcutting. Check that everything has been clamped securely before each cut and keep a notepad record of tooth spacings if you have more than eight divisions to make. Experienced workers are no better off than the rest of us in this respect. A phone call, a tap on the workshop door, an unidentified noise at the crucial time, and you could find you have a couple of teeth too many – or too few – at the end of your sequence.

Try milling six flats on your test piece and making them fit a spanner. That involves moving the gear wheel four teeth for each cut ($24 \div 6 = 4$). Once you've done this successfully, there'll be no stopping you! There is quite a lot of useful work you can do with this simple device and your lathe.

13 COOLANT PUMP

We've stressed the importance of having an adequate supply of coolant flowing over the work, and the toolpoint, when you're turning steels. It's worthwhile saying again that you'll get a better surface finish and a sharp tool will keep its edge longer with coolant than without. It isn't just a matter of cooling the work and the tool. Though this is important, we could dribble plain water over them to get the same result. It's also a matter of lubricating the swarf to make it slide over the cutting edges. Try turning aluminium alloys with high speed steel tools but no coolant or other cutting oil, and you'll see what we mean. The build-up of material on the tool point has to be scraped or chipped off frequently, or the surface finish goes haywire. A spot of paraffin, or even soapy water, on the job makes all the difference.

If getting the coolant on to the job has been a problem, our final project will be your salvation. We're going to make a simple, but impressive electric coolant pump. When we say

Fig. 116. The centrifugal coolant pump being tested in its specially made test-tank. Note the safety connector (right) for connecting up motors which don't have their own plugs fitted.

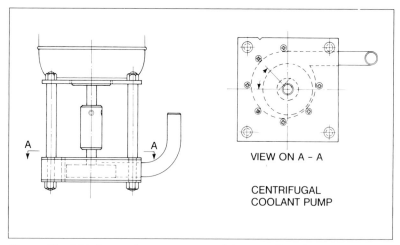

VIEW ON A - A

CENTRIFUGAL
COOLANT PUMP

Above *Fig. 117. General arrangement of the centrifugal coolant pump.*

Right *Fig. 118. Details of the centrifugal coolant pump.*

'electric', we mean it will be driven by its own electric motor, independently of the motor which drives your lathe. The photograph (**Fig. 116**) shows the motor we used, which was from a surplus equipment supplier and cost about half what a new one would have cost. More about motors, later. Now for the pump itself.

To avoid an outbreak of culture-shock, we'd better explain why the body of our pump was made out of cast acrylic block rather than metal. We were testing a motor for centrifugal pump applications, a couple of years ago, and we needed to be able to see what was happening to the impeller while the liquid was passing through. We found crystal clear acrylic block was easy to machine to a superb finish, it kept to dimensions after prolonged use and – this was the crucial consideration – we'd had a whole pile of the stuff given to us earlier in the year.

The plastic commonly known as 'Acrylic' is polymethyl methacrylate, manufactured in the UK and USA under the trade marks 'Perspex' and 'Plexiglas'. It is a fairly hard, brittle material with good machining characteristics using HSS tools and takes an excellent finish from a sharp tool. A disadvantage is its tendency to blunt cutting tools rather rapidly. After machining, an acrylic surface can be brought to a mirror finish – with good optical quality in clear 'Perspex' – by using fine grades of wet-and-dry paper followed by a silver polish such as 'Silvo' or 'Brasso'. Acrylic materials can be bought from plastics suppliers such as Visijar Tucker, who have depots all over the country. Alternatively, firms making plastic signs and display fittings for the trade may sell you offcuts at a good price.

Please yourself what material you use for the body, bearing in mind weight, ease of machining, durability in use and all the

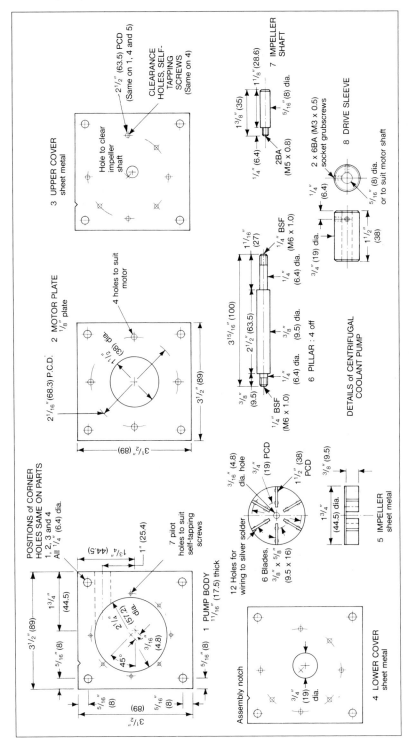

other factors involved. One of the advantages of acrylic is that you can make excellent cemented joints with the correct adhesive. Your first job is to bring the acrylic block to size, 3½ in (89 mm) square, and mark it out. A word of warning, before you drill the four holes at the corners: centre punching is outlawed when you're working with acrylic. This kind of mechanical shock could leave residual damage which would later develop into stress cracks. At worst, it could mean the block would disintegrate after a while. We coated the surfaces with opaque white and marked out in soft pencil.

As we will be making the three layers of the pump 'sandwich' and the motor plate, all at once, we would drill all the corner holes first, to clear the threads on the pillars. It isn't really practical, in this instance, to use our usual procedure – clamping the layers together and drilling all at one setting – so we've gone for the roundabout way. We suggest you next mark out and drill the motor plate, the upper cover and the lower cover, in turn, being especially careful with the positioning of the corner holes. The tapping holes for self tapping screws in the upper and lower surfaces of the body can be spotted from the covers and then drilled to a size and depth to suit the screws you have available. Since this is a machine which may need maintenance in the future (the distant future, we hope), we opted to use 'Phillips' headed screws; slotted screws do not respond well to dismantling, losing the edges of their slots with only minor mishandling. We recommend cruciform-head screws and a cross-point screwdriver as the ideal combination.

The motor plate is made from ⅛ in (3.2 mm) hot rolled MS sheet because it has to carry the weight of quite a hefty motor. (Ours is a comparatively small one, but it weighs 7 lbs (3.18 kg). The covers are made from 17SWG (1.42 mm) steel sheet. Do all the marking out at one sitting, and check at each stage that you have recognised the different positions of the impeller centre and the centre of the cavity in the body. The notches in the top left-hand corner of each part should help with assembly later. Let's call the cavity the 'snail'. The snail centre is offset ³⁄₁₆ in (4.8 mm) from the impeller centre (**Fig. 118**) at an angle of 45°. The only times you'll need to use the snail centre is when you set out the snail itself and when you set out the holes for the self-tapping screws. Their pitch circle is struck from the snail centre, *not* from the impeller centre. Check twice - drill once!

The snail is a simple proposition. First drill and tap the ½ in (12.7 mm) dia hole, 1½ in (38.1 mm) deep from the side, for your deliver elbow. You've drilled holes at the corners of the 3½ in (89 mm) square block which you can use to bolt it to a faceplate with about ¼ in (6.4 mm) of packing under it for boring. Since you weren't able to use a centre punch to mark centres, you'll have to use the surface gauge method (**Fig. 119**) when you set the snail centre to run true. *WATCH out* for the other centre (centre point of impeller). With a dead centre in the

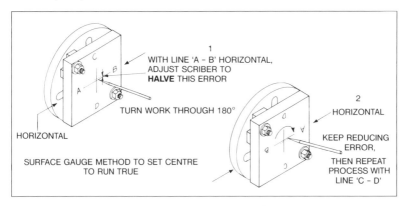

WITH LINE 'A - B' HORIZONTAL,
ADJUST SCRIBER TO
HALVE THIS ERROR

TURN WORK THROUGH 180°

HORIZONTAL

SURFACE GAUGE METHOD TO SET CENTRE
TO RUN TRUE

HORIZONTAL

KEEP REDUCING
ERROR,

THEN REPEAT
PROCESS WITH
LINE 'C - D'

tailstock, set the cross lines almost true. Clamp the block lightly
at first and swing the faceplate until the cross lines lie horizontal
and vertical. Put the base of the surface gauge on the bed shears
and set the point to the height of the horizontal line. Turn the
work through 180° and try the scriber point against the line.
Move the point with the fine-adjustment screw on the surface
gauge base until it has removed *half* the difference between the
two positions. Now adjust the position of the block on the
faceplate, to coincide with the scriber point, and go through the
same sequence until the scriber point hits the line dead-on each
time you rotate the work. Go through the same procedure with
the other line, check that both lines satisfy your test, finally
tighten the nuts and you're ready to roll.

Using a slow speed at first and paraffin wax as a lubricant,
bore out the cavity and leave it with as fine a finish as you can
manage. Breaking into the delivery hole shouldn't give you
much of a problem if you're careful when you hear the warning
sounds. Take it steadily and you'll be fine (**Fig. 120**). When the

Above *Fig. 119. The
surface gauge
method for setting
cross-lines to run
true.*

Right *Fig. 120. The
acrylic 'snail' being
bored. Note the
delivery hole break-
in at the rear of the
bored hole.*

snail is bored out, take off the razor sharp corners from the outside edges and put the block aside while you turn your attention to the impeller (**Fig. 118**). Cut out a 1¾ in × 17SWG (44.5 mm × 1.42 mm) disc of sheet steel, put it on a stub mandrel and skim the diameter.

The secret of success, when putting together the impeller, is the pattern of ⅛ in (3.2 mm) drilled holes in the disc. **Fig. 121** shows how these are used to wire the blades to the disc and hole them firmly in their correct positions for silver soldering. We would still advise marking all the blade positions clearly on the disc and checking that the blades are wired to coincide with those marks, before starting soldering. Any sizeable errors in positioning could lead to severe vibration the first time you run your pump under its own power.

Silver soldering is really beyond the scope of this book, but we can give you some hints to make things easier. Flux both parts of any joint before wiring or clamping. In the case of our impeller it is not vital to keep the solder from flowing away from its appointed place, so you can be liberal with the flux. When the assembly is all fluxed and wired up, cut a short piece of solder wire – say ³⁄₁₆ in (4.8 mm) long and 'glue' it with flux at the junction of blade and disc. Do this for each blade until all the blades have a small piece of solder. File a short taper on the end of a piece of ¼ in (6.4 mm) diameter bar and adjust its shape until you can tap the disc of the impeller on to it and it will be firmly held for heating. Make sure the piece of bar is long enough to prevent heat reaching your fingers. Wear goggles, gloves, apron and safety shoes when you're doing jobs like silver soldering. And have a bucket of water (and/or sand) handy, too. If you're really well equipped you'll have the correct type of fire extinguisher available already.

Play the propane torch on the *underside* of the disc, all the time rotating the bar between your fingers. Don't spin it too

Left *Fig. 121. Close-up of the impeller all wired-up for silver soldering. The pieces of silver solder can be seen 'glued' to the junctions of blades and disc. The slow taper on the rod end grips the disc for heating (bottom right).*

Right *Fig. 122. Assembly of the impeller shaft to the drive motor.*

quickly or, when the flux begins to bubble and melt, the bits of solder will be thrown off. Try it for a few seconds until you get the hang of it before you apply the full heat of the torch.

By the time the solder melts and runs along the joints, the assembly will be glowing dull red. When you're sure all the joints are made, plunge the whole thing into cold water. This not only cools it down rapidly, it also removes excess flux which could be a problem. Now all you need to do is clip off the wires, clean up the impeller with a small rotary wire brush in your electric drill and examine the joints. Any blobs of solder can be filed down at the balancing stage but, first, let's make the impeller shaft.

On looking at **Fig. 118**, you might wonder why we didn't make the sleeve and the impeller shaft out of a single piece of bar. This would be fine, except for the problem of concentricity. The motor shaft, the impeller shaft and the sleeve which connects them, must all be concentric or the assembly will rattle alarmingly on the first test run. We judged the surest way of achieving concentricity to be the three-part procedure shown in **Fig. 122**. The motor shaft is first measured with a micrometer, the impeller shaft is turned to the same diameter and the sleeve is turned, drilled and bored to suit the shafts before parting off. To ensure concentricity use 7⁄8 in (22.2 mm) dia bar and machine the sleeve all at the one setting of the chuck. You can, of course, turn the sleeve end-for-end in the chuck to tidy up the rear face and put on a chamfer. Neither of these operations will grossly affect the concentricity of the finished sleeve.

When the motor shaft and the impeller shaft are both a close sliding fit in the sleeve and you have drilled and tapped it for its grubscrews, the impeller shaft can be cemented into the lower end with anaerobic adhesive, so that it exactly half-fills the bore of the sleeve. (Make sure the grubscrews are short enough to sit well below the surface of the sleeve when they are tightened on

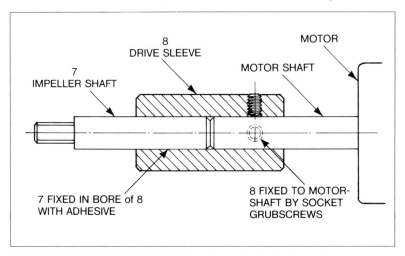

to the motor shaft.) The time has come to assemble the impeller to its shaft with a nut – *but not* a spring washer at this stage. Spring washers are designed to bite into surfaces of both nut and component to prevent loosening. This is not what we want for trial assembly! We may have to release the nut and retighten it several times before we are satisfied with its balance on the shaft. Keep spinning the impeller and its sleeve and shaft on parallels until there is no noticeable heavy side. Adjustments can be made by filing away excess silver solder and by removing a little metal from the ends of the blades which appear to be heavy. Remove the nut on completing this process, and fit a suitable spring washer or star washer before slipping the impeller shaft through the hole in the upper cover (make sure it's the right one and that it's the right way up) and attaching the impeller in its correct position.

Set everything else aside now, and make the four pillars. If you need to re-familiarise yourself with the processes of cutting to length, turning the thread diameters to a uniform shoulder length for all four pillars and cutting the threads with your travelling die holder, now is the time to go back and check.

It's not a good idea to rely on metal to metal (or, rather, metal to plastics) joints when we're dealing with liquids under pressure. The pressure generated by this particular pump is not high but there is some pressure and it has to be taken into account in the construction of the body. We used a commercial jointing compound (one that doesn't set hard) bought from a plumbers' merchant, to seal the surfaces of the top and bottom covers to the acrylic snail. Don't use too much – it will only squeeze out and get all over everything – use just enough to make a visibly sealed joint when all your self-tapping screws are tightened up. Slipping a scrap of ¼ in (6.4 mm) diameter bar into each of the four corner holes will hold the sections in alignment while you screw them together.

Attach the motor plate to the motor in a position where it will not foul anything, and assemble the pillars to the motor plate with locking washers under the nuts. Offer up the pump assembly to the pillars, taking care to align the impeller sleeve with the motor shaft before you finally add the locking washers and nuts to the lower end of the pillars. Spin the impeller between thumb and finger, to check its freedom, screw everything up tight, including the two grubscrews in the impeller sleeve, fit the elbow, attach delivery hose, and Bob's your uncle! **(Fig. 117)**

All you have to do now is to wire up a suitable switch control to your motor and you can run your first tests **(Fig. 123)**. Run the pump dry at first to check that all is well, then you can fill the coolant tank until the liquid level is over halfway up the pillars when the pump is standing on its base on the tank bottom. The liquid level must always be kept below the motor casing, for reasons we shouldn't need to spell out. Lead the delivery hose

Fig. 123. Underside view of the coolant pump showing the suction hole and the 'eye' of the impeller.

away to a safe disposal point, such as the lathe swarf tray, or lead it back into the tank. Switch on and watch the coolant cascade from the end of the delivery hose. You'll be surprised how much liquid this unit can deliver. Our tests on the pump showed that it will move 5 gal of liquid from one container to another in 4 min 36 sec – more than enough for a home mechanic's purposes. So you'll need a control valve at the outfeed end of the hose. A valve is usually supplied with commercial systems and these can be bought from ironmongers or on the surplus equipment market.

Electric motors, too, are widely available and you only have to give your supplier details of what you expect the motor to do, for him to pick out just the one. If not, try another supplier. There are one or two things you should watch out for: first of all, specify your local mains voltage – don't buy motors that run on other voltages or frequencies than the supply in your workshop, unless you have the training to cope with any necessary modifications; secondly, buy a continuously rated motor, not one that can only handle short, spaced out, periods of work. As we are not electrical experts, that's all the advice we're going to offer. If you're in doubt, find a friendly electrician or electrical shop to see you through. (In the reading list we have included a useful book on electric motors.)

We have enjoyed involving you in the various projects in this book and we hope you will go on to gain more and more experience in the processes and techniques we have outlined. Above all, we believe that metalworking should be enjoyed. We hope that what begins here, as a passing interest, will go on to become a lifetime's love affair.

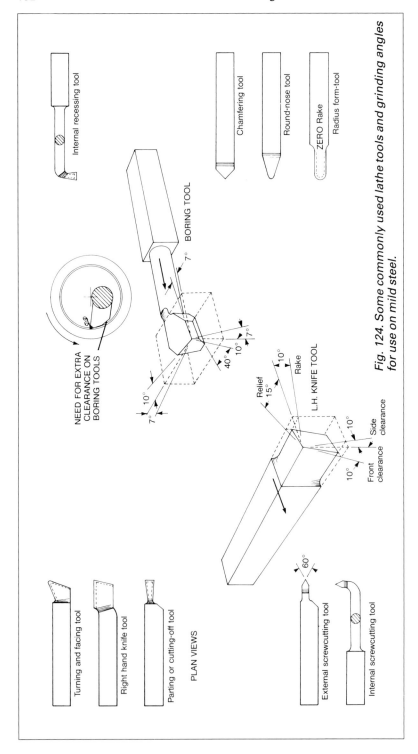

Fig. 124. Some commonly used lathe tools and grinding angles for use on mild steel.

GLOSSARY

Afrormosia A hard African timber similar in colour to teak

Allen screw A screw with a hexagonal socket in the head to fit an Allen key

Anaerobic adhesive A type of engineering adhesive which sets only in the absence of air

Angle plate An L-shaped casting with machined vertical and horizontal reference surfaces and slots for bolts

Annealed Metal with residual hardness and stresses taken out by heat treatment

Arbor A cylindrical stem for holding slitting saws and for turning discs and hollow work in the lathe. (*See Mandrel*)

Arbor press A device for inserting arbors. (*See Mandrel press*)

Auto feed The means of moving the saddle of a lathe under power

BA The British Association thread type, with an angle of 47°

Backlash The free movement of feed screws and gears before motion is transmitted

Back gear Extra-slow speed gearing on a lathe headstock

Ball pein hammer A hammer with one straight face and one rounded face

Bezel A fixed or moveable ring around the face of an instrument

Blind hole A hole which doesn't pass through the material

BMS (or BDMS) Bright drawn mild steel

Boring head A cutting head to fit into machine spindles for boring

Boss The thickening at the centre of a wheel to strengthen the spindle hole

BSW The British Standard Whitworth thread. A coarse thread with a 55° angle

BSF The British Standard Fine thread, of Whitworth form with an angle of 55°

Bush A tubular insert to reduce the bore of a hole

Cap screw A fixing screw, usually of high tensile steel, with a tall cheese head in which is forged a hexagonal socket for an Allen key. The outer diameter of the head is often ribbed or knurled.

Carbide tips Disposable cutting tips made from extremely hard materials such as Tungsten Carbide

Centre height The height of the lathe mandrel axis above the ways

Centre punch A punch for making conical depressions in metal for marking out and machining

Chamfer The removal of the corner of a workpiece at 45°

Changewheels Loose gears supplied with a lathe and used to set up trains for screwcutting

Chucking piece Extra metal left on a workpiece for holding it in a chuck

Collars Thick-walled bushes, sometimes fixed over shafts with screws

Collet A split bush for gripping work inside a tapered housing

Counterbore An enlarged-diameter extension to a hole or bore

Countersink The conical depression at the top of a hole to take the screw head. Also the tool for cutting this depression

Curing time High-tech adhesives first set, then cure, over a period of hours or days

Datum A reference point, line or surface from which other marking or measuring is done

Deburr To take off the burred edges resulting from cutting operations

Deflection The movement of a machine element or part of a structure under load.

Die A tool for cutting external threads on rods

Dividing Arranging for a given number of holes or graduations to be equally spaced on a circle

Drift A soft metal bar used to avoid hammer-marking of the work

DTI (or 'clock') The dial test indicator. An instrument for showing very small differences in position on a circular scale

Elephant's foot A tip fitted to the plunger of a DTI when it is being used to indicate against curved surfaces

End load For example, the load on the headstock bearings when drilling from the tailstock in the lathe

End mill A milling cutter which cuts on its diameter and at the end

End play Axial movement of a shaft in its bearings

Engineers' blue A blue marking paste for showing up high and low spots

Epoxy resin Strong, chemically resistant synthetic resin adhesive

Fillet A radius to strengthen the junction of two surfaces of a casting

Fixture A device attached to a machine table to hold work for machining

Flanges The flared-out edges of metal sheets or ends of pipes for jointing and fastening

Free cutting MS Mild steel with a high sulphur content to facilitate rapid machining

Full nut A nut whose height is about the same as the bolt diameter

Geared head lathe A lathe in which all spindle speeds are obtained by gear changes instead of belts and pulleys

Grubscrew A screw with no head, for tightening gears etc on to shafts

Half nuts A split nut, moveable with a lever, for engaging and disengaging auto feed

Helical Having the form of a helix

Helix The line traced by a point which moves at uniform speed along a rotating cylinder

Hot rolled steel Mild steel used straight from the rolling mill with no cold working

Indexing Arranging to move machined faces into selected angular relationships, e.g, hexagons and squares

In situ Remaining in place while further work is done on it

Jeweller's loupe A low-power magnifying glass held in the eye socket

Jig A device for presenting a workpiece for machining, with provision to guide the cutting tools. *(See Fixture)*

Key A flat piece of metal inserted to hold one component fast to another

Keyway A housing cut in a component to take a key

Knurling The design produced on a turned surface by patterned wheels biting into it

Lead The taper on the tip of a cutting tool to allow gradual entry into the work, eg tap or reamer
The amount of forward movement of a nut in one complete revolution on its bolt

Leadscrew The threaded rod along a lathe bed which drives the saddle in auto feed

Locking washer A type of washer with hardened teeth to bite into both nut and component, preventing loosening

Locknut •A nut with a plastic insert or drag-slot to prevent loosening
•Two nuts, driven one on to the other to prevent loosening

Mandrel An alternative name for *Arbor*

Mandrel bore The hole passing through the headstock spindle of a lathe

Mandrel press *See Arbor press and Arbor*

Marking blue A quick-drying blue liquid used to coat bright metal surfaces for marking out

Morse taper A taper of approx ⅝ in per foot (52.8 mm per metre) used on the shanks of twist drills and other tooling

Neat cutting oil A cutting lubricant, used without being diluted.

Nibbling Taking out shapes from sheet metal by small 'bites' with a cutting tool

Oil retaining bush A bearing bush made of sintered metal in which its porous structure retains lubricants

PCD Pitch circle diameter, for rings of drilled holes, etc

Pin punch A parallel-bladed punch for driving pins into, and out of, holes

Plug gauge An accurately sized cylinder, which can be inserted into holes to gauge bores

Polygon A many-sided figure

Profile cutting Cutting steel plate to a template with flame cutting equipment

Pump centrefinder A centring point with a spring-loaded centre-hole

Quickchange gearbox A gearbox for screwcutting on the lathe without need for changewheels

Quickchange toolpost A toolpost in which tools are in separate holders that return them to the toolpost at centre height

Quenching Quickly reducing the metal temperature in heat treatment, by plunging into water or oil

Quill The same form of component as a sleeve, but a quill usually has some driving function (eg, in a drill press)

Radius A rounded end, edge or fillet on a component

Ratchet and pawl An escapement device (eg, on lifting gear) to prevent the chain or rope overrunning

Rhomboid Lozenge-shaped

Ring gauge A ring having an accurately-sized hole for gauging diameters

Riveting Joining two components with a soft metal-headed pin, spread over by hammer blows

Rose bit A crude type of countersinking tool

Rotary table A fixture with a circular, graduated sub-table, for moving the workpiece along an arc during machining operations

Running centre A type of tailstock centre which rotates with the work on precision bearings

Scribing block (or surface gauge) A scriber carried in universal clamps on a pillar mounted on a solid base with fine adjustments

Scribing gauge Identical in principle with the joiner's marking gauge, but with all metal construction and a hardened scribing point

Self grip pliers Pliers which can be clamped on to workpieces to hold them for machining and released by pressing a spring loaded lever

Shank The part of a cutting tool that fits into the holder, chuck or machine spindle

Shim Accurately thicknessed steel or brass sheet used for precise packings, etc

Side load The cutting pressure on machine spindle bearings from moving the work at right angles to the spindle axis

Silver steel A high carbon steel (about 1.1% carbon) of ground 'silvery' finish, hence the name. Does not contain silver

Sintering Forming components from powdered metal which has been heated and compressed but not melted

Sleeve A cylindrical or conical shell which fills the annular space between two round components of different sizes and holds them together. *(See MT sleeve)*

Slip blocks (slip gauges) Accurately ground pieces of steel, made in sets, used in inspection, measurement and setting up

Slitting saw A disc-shaped milling cutter with teeth on the circumference

Slot drill A similar milling cutter to an end mill which can be fed downwards into the work to start a slot

Soft jaws Pads fitted to vices to prevent the serrated steel jaws marking finished work

Solid centres Hardened and ground centres for headstock and tailstock, with taper shanks to fit sockets

Spigot A projection on a component, which fits into a depression in the mating component, for location

Splines Sector-shaped longitudinal grooves cut in a shaft to suit mating grooves inside a gear or collar

Split pin A closed, bent wire pin the end of which can be spread open when pushed through a hole in a shaft or screw

Stub arbor An arbor with provision to hold the work, or a cutter, close up to the chuck jaws

Stub mandrel As above

Studding Rods with threads cut along their whole length

Surface gauge *(See Scribing block)*

Tap A tool for cutting threads inside drilled holes

Template A pattern used to transfer angles or shapes from drawings on to the work

Tenon A strip of metal on the base of a machine attachment which locates in a slot on the machine table

Tension file Slender wires with teeth cut on their outer surface, held in a frame to cut irregular shapes from sheet metal

Thread A continuous helical groove cut inside a hole or on the surface of a round bar

Thread chaser A tool for finishing threads to accurate form

Three square file A file of triangular section

Tommy bar A captive or loose bar used to apply leverage

Toolmaker's clamps Small clamps in which pressure is applied while keeping the bar jaws parallel

Toolpost drilling attachment A drilling spindle with an independent drive attached to a lathe toolpost

TPI Threads per inch

Traverse To move the cutting tool from the beginning of the cut to its end

Waisted Reduced in diameter at some point

Wiggler A device to magnify errors in centring of a workpiece in the lathe, making them clearly visible to the operator

Witness line An 'indicator' line to show position and limits, etc, on workpieces undergoing machining, and on machine movements

'Zeus' tables Tables of information on threads and drills, etc, in booklet form

SUGGESTED READING

MAGAZINES

Engineering In Miniature
Live Steam (USA)
Model Engineer
Modeltec (USA)
Projects In Metal (USA)
The Home Shop Machinist (USA)

(Subscription agents for US magazines: Camden Miniature Steam Services, Rode, Bath, Somerset.)

BOOKS

Building the Universal Pillartool, Geo H. Thomas (Argus)*
Dividing and Graduating, Geo H. Thomas (TEE Publishing)
Electric Motors, Jim Cox (Argus)
General Engineering Workshop Practice (Odham's Press, 1952)*
Hardening, Tempering and Heat Treatment, Tubal Cain (Argus)
Introducing The Lathe, Stan Bray (Patrick Stephens Ltd, 1984)*
Sheet Metal Work, R. E. Wakeford (Argus)
The Amateur's Lathe, L. Sparey (Argus)
The Myford Lathe Manual, I. Bradley (Argus)
Workshop Technology (4 vols), W. A. J. Chapman (Edward Arnold)*

*denotes titles out of print

INDEX

Figures in brackets denote pages with illustrations